THE TENNYSON RECITER

EDITED BY

ALFRED H. MILES

To Tom Hedworth Story

from
Nucle Clive

Christmas 1903

THE
TENNYSON
RECITER

EDITED BY

ALFRED H. MILES

LONDON
HUTCHINSON & CO
34 PATERNOSTER ROW
1901

PRINTED BY
HAZELL, WATSON, AND VINEY, LD.,
LONDON AND AYLESBURY

TO THE QUEEN

REVERED, beloved—O you that hold
    A nobler office upon earth
    Than arms, or power of brain, or birth
Could give the warrior kings of old,

Victoria,—since your Royal grace
    To one of less desert allows
    This laurel greener from the brows
Of him that utter'd nothing base ;

And should your greatness, and the care
    That yokes with empire, yield you time
    To make demand of modern rhyme
If aught of ancient worth be there ;

Then—while a sweeter music wakes,
    And thro' wild March the throstle calls,
    Where all about your palace-walls
The sun-lit almond-blossom shakes—

Take, Madam, this poor book of song ;
    For tho' the faults were thick as dust
    In vacant chambers, I could trust
Your kindness. May you rule us long,

To the Queen

And leave us rulers of your blood
   As noble till the latest day !
   May children of our children say,
"She wrought her people lasting good ;

" Her court was pure ; her life serene ;
   God gave her peace ; her land reposed ;
   A thousand claims to reverence closed
In her as Mother, Wife and Queen ;

" And statesmen at her council met
   Who knew the seasons when to take
   Occasion by the hand, and make
The bounds of freedom wider yet

" By shaping some august decree,
   Which kept her throne unshaken still,
   Broad-based upon her people's will,
And compass'd by the inviolate sea."

March, 1851.

CONTENTS

8   Contents

INTRODUCTION

THE prophets were the poets of old time, and the poets are the prophets of ours. As such they have always been the pioneers of human progress ;—the statesman and the philosopher but follow them afar off.

The statesman deals with things that are, and occupies us with the study of the real ; the poet treats of things that may be, and inspires us with visions of the ideal : the statesman is as the hand of one groping amid jungle-growths of selfish interests seeking the adjustment of law ; the poet is as the voice of one crying in the wilderness, prepare ye the way of love !

To those who suffer in real life, trust in possible ideals is saving faith, and beautiful upon the mountains are the feet of them that bring good tidings. Poetry is the herald of hope's full fruition, and as such the inspiration of faith's unceasing toil.

The statesman may, and often does, seek his own advantage or that of the class to which he belongs. Commerce is admittedly competitive, and men of business without compunction seek their own gain in the calculated loss of others. Official Christianity, which draws its political power from the one and its financial support from the other, condones the modified barbarism which survives in competitive institutions—a barbarism, as compared with older forms, less brutal in its methods, but more cruel in its results. The poet knows no competition but emulation, and that in the demonstration of beauty and the cause of love. It is only by the sacrifice of his poetry that the poet can become selfish. This so, the true poet is the best of all preachers of the best of all gospels for the people.

It is those, however, who most of all need the comfortable message of the poet who from one cause or another have the least access to it, the least ability to appreciate it, and the least opportunity to enjoy it. Among major causes are the inexorable demands of labour, which exhaust energy and leave no leisure for thought ; and the pitiless environment of labour, which glooms the uplook of the night of sorrow and walls in the outlook of the day of pain.

That the statesman, following the poet's lead, has done something to ameliorate the lot of labour is of course true ; but much remains to be done, and the labourer himself needs to be prepared for the larger liberty he is destined ultimately to enjoy. In this work of education, too, the poet is the best teacher of the people ; and we have much to hope for from the familiarisation of the masses with the best thoughts and ideals of the ages, and the opening up to them of the well of English undefiled.

Other causes of the neglect of poetry by those who have the most need for it and the most to hope from it may be more easily removed. Among these is the general inaccessibility of the poets in a form at once within simple means, ordinary application, and average comprehension—easy to purchase, easy to read, and easy to understand. Inexpensive editions of the poets are legion, and if the numbers purchased were only read there would be small room to complain of the neglect of poetry. But the "cheap idea," which crams the whole of a poet's writings into one crowded volume, in a type which no one can read with comfort, and often prints it upon paper which reveals the type on both sides of the leaf at once, produces books which are bought and given away, it may be, but which are seldom read and never read with comfort.

The poets for the people must be printed in good type, well spaced, upon opaque paper, and be published at a low price; and the selection must be made with a view to those for whom it is intended. It is not the whole of a poet's writings that one wants in a volume for this purpose, but the best of them selected from a popular point of view. The proper place for the complete works of a poet is the reference library.

Of such a series the present is the initial volume. The type and form witness their own advantages, and the selection makes its own appeal. It is not an anthology of the poet's choicest flowers culled by the hand of criticism for the enjoyment of the few; it is a selection made for popular purposes from such available poems as, in the judgment of the Editor, are most likely to appeal to the widest circle. As such it includes many of the poems which won for Tennyson his earlier recognition and some which he never afterwards surpassed.

To those who "do not think much of poetry" the song, the ballad, and the story in verse are the most likely to appeal. The simple ballad of "Lady Clare" may be "a thing of beauty and a joy for ever" to many who would miss the charm of "Œnone" or "The Lotus Eaters"; and the song

"Break, break, break," may give expression to the heart-throb of millions who would find no consolation in the noble faith of "In Memoriam." For this reason the selection has been made from the dramatic point of view, and the book is offered to the Reciter, who may be a true missionary to those who do not read verse for themselves. Thus stories in verse occupy a large number of the following pages. "Lady Clare," with its un-obtrusive but ever popular moral,—love levels all; "The Lord of Burleigh," with its sweet-sad romance of real life; "The May Queen" and its additions, with their pathetic teaching of the vanity of vanity; and "Dora," with its true pictures of country life. To these, to name no others, are added "Godiva," "A Dream of Fair Women," "The Charge of the Light Brigade," and "The Ode on the Death of the Duke of Wellington,"—poems based upon historic incidents, and therefore having a concrete interest for those to whom fancy and imagination do not of themselves appeal; and such introductions to the Arthurian legends as "The Lady of Shalott," "Sir Galahad," and the "Morte d'Arthur," together with "A Day-Dream," "Locksley Hall," and the lyric monodrama "Maud."

To name these alone is to name a large number of poems which are great favourites with many people who will not regret to see them in their present popular and readable form, and also to name those which in the Editor's judgment are of available poems the best calculated to introduce the poet favourably to new readers.

ALFRED H. MILES.

ALFRED TENNYSON

1809—1892

ALFRED TENNYSON was born at Somersby, near
Horncastle, in Lincolnshire, on the 6th of August, 1809.
The poet's father, the Rev. George Clayton Tennyson, LL.D.,
was rector of Somersby and Enderby, and vicar of Great
Grimsby, and his mother was a daughter of the Rev. Stephen
Fytche, sometime vicar of Louth.

The home at Somersby, which was beautifully situated
in the midst of picturesque scenery, was one of no ordinary
culture and happiness. The elder Tennyson was a man
of fine character and intellectual attainment, and his wife,
to quote a poetic generalisation, "a sweet and gentle and
most imaginative woman." From these two sprang a family
of poets. The eldest-born died young; but the second
son, Frederick, born in 1807, proved himself a poet of
no mean order; and Charles Tennyson, the third son, born
in 1808, was the poetic partner of Alfred, the fourth son, in
the publication of "Poems by Two Brothers" in 1827.

Frederick Tennyson was contemporary with Mr. Gladstone
at Eton, and was captain of the school in 1827. Sir
Francis Doyle, who was a schoolfellow with them, speaks
of Frederick as being "a remarkable boy among his senior
contemporaries."

Charles Tennyson, who on the death of his great-uncle,
Samuel Turner, of Caistor, succeeded to his estate, and who
added the name of his benefactor to his own, followed his
father's profession, and became vicar of Grasby, where he
spent many happy years in the strenuous discharge of
clerical duty.

At the age of seven Alfred left the home at Somersby to
live with his maternal grandmother at Louth, that he might

attend the grammar-school of that town. There he continued for four years. At eleven years of age he returned to Somersby, where he studied with his father until he went to college. While quite young he became an omnivorous reader, and he was fortunate in having access to a liberal library. Under these circumstances it is scarcely surprising that, gifted with imagination, he began to write early. Thomson, Pope, and Scott seem to have inspired him by turns, and one ambitious effort of six thousand lines in the style of Scott drew from his father the remark, " If Alfred die, one of our greatest poets will have gone."

In 1827 the Tennyson brothers made their first appeal to the wider world outside the home circle by the publication, through Messrs. J. & J. Jackson, of Louth, of " Poems by Two Brothers." This volume, for which the young poets received £20, half in cash and half in books, contained four poems by Frederick, the remainder of the book being contributed by Charles and Alfred.

In the following year Charles and Alfred matriculated at Trinity College, Cambridge, where they became acquainted with a number of young men who, like themselves, were destined to become famous in art and letters. Among these were Monckton Milnes (afterwards Lord Houghton), Trench (afterwards Dean of Westminster and Archbishop of Dublin), and Arthur Hallam, son of the historian, who was described by Alfred as " as near perfection as mortal man could be," and whose early death at Vienna, while travelling with his father, in 1833, inspired one of Alfred's noblest poems, " In Memoriam."

In 1829 Alfred won the Chancellor's medal with a poem on Timbuctoo, and in the following year he published his " Poems," chiefly lyrical, a small volume of one hundred and fifty pages, which included the " Ode to Memory," " The Poet," " Claribel," " Mariana," the " Recollections of the Arabian Nights," and " The Ballad of Oriana." This volume was favourably noticed by Sir John Browning in the *Westminster Review*, by Leigh Hunt in the *Tatler*, and by Arthur Hallam in the *Englishman's Magazine*.

In 1831 Alfred left college without taking a degree, and a month later his father died suddenly.

"Poems by Alfred Tennyson," his next volume, appeared in 1832. It included "The Lady of Shalott," "The Miller's Daughter," "Œnone," "The Palace of Art," "The Lotus Eaters," and "A Dream of Fair Women." The volume was unfavourably reviewed in the *Quarterly* and elsewhere.

The death of Arthur Hallam, who had meanwhile become engaged to his sister, in 1833, very powerfully affected Tennyson's mind. It inspired "The Two Voices; or, Thoughts of a Suicide," as well as the greater poem "In Memoriam," which was slowly perfected through the years and did not appear in print until 1850.

In 1836 Charles Tennyson, who graduated in 1832, and was ordained in 1835, married Louisa, daughter of Henry Sellwood, a solicitor of Horncastle. At the wedding ceremony Alfred attended the bride's sister Emily, who acted as bridesmaid. On this occasion the first thoughts of marriage are said to have entered Alfred's mind, though they were not consummated until 1850, fourteen years later, when he married Emily Sellwood at Shiplake-on-the-Thames.

"Poems," in two volumes, was the next work issued, and this in 1842. For these volumes Tennyson went carefully over his earlier poems, re-writing some and improving others, and adding such important poems as "Locksley Hall," "Godiva," "The Vision of Sin," "Ulysses," "Sir Galahad," and "Morte d'Arthur." These volumes brought the poet increasing fame and wider recognition; but their issue was followed by the failure of some speculations in which the family were interested—a failure which involved them in loss and hardship. Under these !circumstances relief was procured in the form of a Civil List pension of £200, granted by Sir Robert Peel at the instance of the poet's old college friend, Monckton Milnes.

In 1847 "The Princess" was published, and in 1850 "In Memoriam" appeared anonymously. This latter poem created wide interest and no little controversy, and, on acknowledgment, added greatly to the poet's fame. In this year, too, Wordsworth died, and upon the refusal of the Laureateship by Samuel Rogers, it was offered to Tennyson, who accepted it. In 1853 he removed to Farringford, Freshwater, Isle of Wight.

The poet's next volume appeared in 1855, and contained "The Brook," "The Daisy," "The Ode on the Death of the Duke of Wellington," written in 1851, and "The Charge of the Light Brigade," which was first printed in the *Examiner* on the 9th of December, 1854. In this same year he was made D.C.L. of Oxford, and published his lyrical monodrama "Maud."

For some years after this Tennyson was busy on the Arthurian legends. "Enid" bears date 1856, "Guinevere" 1858, and "The Idylls of the King" 1859. This latter work met with an instantaneous welcome, and greatly widened and extended the poet's popularity. This year, too, "The Grandmother" appeared, in the pages of a July number of *Once a Week*. "Enoch Arden" was published in 1864, in a volume which also contained "The Northern Farmer" (Old Style). In 1868 Tennyson built himself a house at Aldwick, near Haslemere, and in 1869 published "The Holy Grail," and with it "The Northern Farmer" (New Style). Public recognition followed. Mr. Gladstone offered the poet a baronetcy in 1873, and Mr. Disraeli repeated the offer in 1874; but both offers were declined. "Queen Mary," completed in 1875, was produced at the Lyceum Theatre in 1876, and "Harold" was published during the same year.

In 1880 "Ballads and Poems" appeared, including "The Revenge," "The Defence of Lucknow," "The Children's Hospital," and "The Northern Cobbler." In 1882 "The Promise of May" was produced at the Globe Theatre. In 1884 "The Cup," "The Falcon," and "Becket" appeared in rapid succession. In this year the poet was offered a peerage by Mr. Gladstone, and accepted it. In 1885 "Tiresias, and Other Poems" appeared; in 1886 "The Promise of May" and "Locksley Hall Sixty Years After." In 1889 "Demeter, and Other Poems," including "Crossing the Bar," was issued; and in 1891 his last drama, "Robin Hood" ("The Foresters"), was produced in New York.

Alfred Tennyson died at Farringford on Thursday, the 6th of October, 1892, at 1.35 a.m., and was buried by the side of Robert Browning in Westminster Abbey on Wednesday, October the 12th.

POEMS

BY

LORD TENNYSON

LADY CLARE.

It was the time when lilies blow,
  And clouds are highest up in air,
Lord Ronald brought a lily-white doe
  To give his cousin, Lady Clare.

I trow they did not part in scorn ;
  Lovers long-betroth'd were they ;
They two will wed the morrow morn ;
  God's blessing on the day !

" He does not love me for my birth,
  Nor for my lands so broad and fair ;
He loves me for my own true worth,
  And that is well," said Lady Clare.

In there came old Alice the nurse,
  Said, " Who was this that went from thee ? "
" It was my cousin," said Lady Clare ;
  " To-morrow he weds with me."

" O God be thank'd ! " said Alice the nurse,
  " That all comes round so just and fair :
Lord Ronald is heir of all your lands,
  And you are not the Lady Clare."

" Are ye out of your mind, my nurse, my nurse ? "
  Said Lady Clare, " that ye speak so wild ? "
" As God's above," said Alice the nurse,
  " I speak the truth : you are my child.

" The old Earl's daughter died at my breast ;
  I speak the truth, as I live by bread !
I buried her like my own sweet child,
  And put my child in her stead."

" Falsely, falsely have ye done,
  O mother," she said, " if this be true,
To keep the best man under the sun
  So many years from his due."

" Nay now, my child," said Alice the nurse,
  " But keep the secret for your life,
And all you have will be Lord Ronald's,
  When you are man and wife."

" If I'm a beggar born," she said,
  " I will speak out, for I dare not lie.
Pull off, pull off, the broach of gold,
  And fling the diamond necklace by."

" Nay now, my child," said Alice the nurse,
  " But keep the secret all ye can."
She said " Not so : but I will know
  If there be any faith in man."

" Nay now, what faith ? " said Alice the nurse,
    " The man will cleave unto his right."
" And he shall have it," the lady replied,
    "Tho' I should die to-night."

" Yet give one kiss to your mother dear !
    Alas, my child, I sinn'd for thee."
" O mother, mother, mother," she said,
    " So strange it seems to me.

" Yet here's a kiss for my mother dear,
    My mother dear, if this be so,
And lay your hand upon my head,
    And bless me, mother, ere I go."

She clad herself in a russet gown,
    She was no longer Lady Clare :
She went by dale, and she went by down,
    With a single rose in her hair.

The lily-white doe Lord Ronald had brought
    Leapt up from where she lay,
Dropt her head in the maiden's hand,
    And follow'd her all the way.

Down stept Lord Ronald from his tower :
    " O Lady Clare, you shame your worth !
Why come you drest like a village maid,
    That are the flower of the earth ? "

" If I come drest like a village maid,
    I am but as my fortunes are :
I am a beggar born," she said,
    " And not the Lady Clare."

" Play me no tricks," said Lord Ronald,
  " For I am yours in word and in deed.
Play me no tricks," said Lord Ronald,
  " Your riddle is hard to read."

O and proudly stood she up !
  Her heart within her did not fail:
She look'd into Lord Ronald's eyes,
  And told him all her nurse's tale.

He laugh'd a laugh of merry scorn :
  He turn'd, and kiss'd her where she stood :
" If you are not the heiress born,
  And I," said he, "the next in blood—

" If you are not the heiress born,
  And I," said he, " the lawful heir,
We two will wed to-morrow morn,
  And you shall still be Lady Clare."

THE LORD OF BURLEIGH.

In her ear he whispers gaily,
  " If my heart by signs can tell,
Maiden, I have watch'd thee daily,
  And I think thou lov'st me well."

She replies, in accents fainter,
  " There is none I love like thee."
He is but a landscape-painter,
  And a village maiden she.

He to lips, that fondly falter,
  Presses his without reproof :
Leads her to the village altar,
  And they leave her father's roof.

" I can make no marriage present ;
  Little can I give my wife.
Love will make our cottage pleasant,
  And I love thee more than life."

They by parks and lodges going
  See the lordly castles stand :
Summer woods, about them blowing,
  Made a murmur in the land.

From deep thought himself he rouses,
  Says to her that loves him well,
" Let us see these handsome houses
  Where the wealthy nobles dwell."

So she goes by him attended,
  Hears him lovingly converse,
Sees whatever fair and splendid
  Lay betwixt his home and hers ;

Parks with oak and chestnut shady,
  Parks and order'd gardens great,
Ancient homes of lord and lady,
  Built for pleasure and for state.

All he shows her makes him dearer :
  Evermore she seems to gaze
On that cottage growing nearer,
  Where they twain will spend their days.

O but she will love him truly !
    He shall have a cheerful home ;
She will order all things duly,
    When beneath his roof they come.

Thus her heart rejoices greatly,
    Till a gateway she discerns
With armorial bearings stately,
    And beneath the gate she turns ;

Sees a mansion more majestic
    Than all those she saw before :
Many a gallant gay domestic
    Bows before him at the door.

And they speak in gentle murmur,
    When they answer to his call,
While he treads with footstep firmer,
    Leading on from hall to hall.

And, while now she wonders blindly,
    Nor the meaning can divine,
Proudly turns he round and kindly,
    " All of this is mine and thine."

Here he lives in state and bounty,
    Lord of Burleigh, fair and free,
Not a lord in all the county
    Is so great a lord as he.

All at once the colour flushes
    Her sweet face from brow to chin
As it were with shame she blushes,
    And her spirit changed within.

Then her countenance all over
  Pale again as death did prove :
But he clasp'd her like a lover,
  And he cheer'd her soul with love.

So she strove against her weakness,
  Tho' at times her spirits sank :
Shaped her heart with woman's meekness
  To all duties of her rank :

And a gentle consort made he,
  And her gentle mind was such
That she grew a noble lady,
  And the people loved her much.

But a trouble weigh'd upon her,
  And perplex'd her, night and morn,
With the burthen of an honour
  Unto which she was not born.

Faint she grew, and ever fainter,
  As she murmur'd, " Oh, that he
Were once more that landscape-painter,
  Which did win my heart from me ! "

So she droop'd and droop'd before him,
  Fading slowly from his side :
Three fair children first she bore him,
  Then before her time she died.

Weeping, weeping late and early,
  Walking up and pacing down,
Deeply mourn'd the Lord of Burleigh,
  Burleigh-house by Stamford-town.

And he came to look upon her,
    And he look'd at her and said,
" Bring the dress and put it on her,
    That she wore when she was wed."

Then her people, softly treading,
    Bore to earth her body, drest
In the dress that she was wed in,
    That her spirit might have rest.

THE MAY QUEEN.

You must wake and call me early, call me early,
    mother dear ;
To-morrow 'ill be the happiest time of all the glad
    New-year ;
Of all the glad New-year, mother, the maddest
    merriest day ;
For I'm to be Queen o' the May, mother, I'm to be
    Queen o' the May.

There's many a black black eye, they say, but none
    so bright as mine ;
There's Margaret and Mary, there's Kate and
    Caroline :
But none so fair as little Alice in all the land
    they say,
So I'm to be Queen o' the May, mother, I'm to be
    Queen o' the May.

I sleep so sound all night, mother, that I shall never
    wake,
If you do not call me loud when the day begins
    to break :
But I must gather knots of flowers, and buds and
    garlands gay,
For I'm to be Queen o' the May, mother, I'm to be
    Queen o' the May.

As I came up the valley whom think ye should
    I see,
But Robin leaning on the bridge beneath the hazel-
    tree ?
He thought of that sharp look, mother, I gave him
    yesterday,—
But I'm to be Queen o' the May, mother, I'm to be
    Queen o' the May.

He thought I was a ghost, mother, for I was all
    in white,
And I ran by him without speaking, like a flash of
    light.
They call me cruel-hearted, but I care not what
    they say,
For I'm to be Queen o' the May, mother, I'm to be
    Queen o' the May.

They say he's dying all for love, but that can
    never be :
They say his heart is breaking, mother—what is that
    to me ?

There's many a bolder lad 'ill woo me any summer
  day,
And I'm to be Queen o' the May, mother, I'm to
  be Queen o' the May.

Little Effie shall go with me to-morrow to the
  green,
And you'll be there, too, mother, to see me made
  the Queen ;
For the shepherd lads on every side 'ill come from
  far away,
And I'm to be Queen o' the May, mother, I'm to
  be Queen o' the May.

The honeysuckle round the porch has wov'n its
  wavy bowers,
And by the meadow-trenches blow the faint sweet
  cuckoo-flowers ;
And the wild marsh-marigold shines like fire in
  swamps and hollows gray,
And I'm to be Queen o' the May, mother, I'm to
  be Queen o' the May.

The night-winds come and go, mother, upon the
  meadow-grass,
And the happy stars above them seem to brighten as
  they pass ;
There will not be a drop of rain the whole of the
  livelong day,
And I'm to be Queen o' the May, mother, I'm to
  be Queen o' the May.

All the valley, mother, 'ill be fresh and green and
 still,
And the cowslip and the crowfoot are over all the
 hill,
And the rivulet in the flowery dale 'ill merrily glance
 and play,
For I'm to be Queen o' the May, mother, I'm to be
 Queen o' the May.

So you must wake and call me early, call me early,
 mother dear,
To-morrow 'ill be the happiest time of all the glad
 New-year :
To-morrow 'ill be of all the year the maddest
 merriest day,
For I'm to be Queen o' the May, mother, I'm to be
 Queen o' the May.

NEW-YEAR'S EVE.

If you're waking call me early, call me early, mother
 dear,
For I would see the sun rise upon the glad
 New-year.
It is the last New-year that I shall ever
 see,
Then you may lay me low i' the mould and think
 no more of me.

To-night I saw the sun set : he set and left
 behind
The good old year, the dear old time, and all my
 peace of mind ;

And the New-year's coming up, mother, but I shall
never see
The blossom on the blackthorn, the leaf upon
the tree.

Last May we made a crown of flowers : we had a
merry day ;
Beneath the hawthorn on the green they made me
Queen of May ;
And we danced about the may-pole and in the hazel
copse,
Till Charles's Wain came out above the tall white
chimney-tops.

There's not a flower on all the hills : the frost is on
the pane :
I only wish to live till the snowdrops come
again :
I wish the snow would melt and the sun come out
on high :
I long to see a flower so before the day I
die.

The building rook 'ill caw from the windy tall
elm-tree,
And the tufted plover pipe along the fallow
lea,
And the swallow 'ill come back again with summer
o'er the wave,
But I shall lie alone, mother, within the mouldering
grave.

Upon the chancel-casement, and upon that grave
    of mine,
In the early early morning the summer sun 'ill
    shine,
Before the red cock crows from the farm upon the
    hill,
When you are warm-asleep, mother, and all the
    world is still.

When the flowers come again, mother, beneath the
    waning light
You'll never see me more in the long gray fields
    at night ;
When from the dry dark wold the summer airs
    blow cool
On the oat-grass and the sword-grass, and the
    bulrush in the pool.

You'll bury me, my mother, just beneath the
    hawthorn shade,
And you'll come sometimes and see me where I am
    lowly laid.
I shall not forget you, mother, I shall hear you when
    you pass,
With your feet above my head in the long and
    pleasant grass.

I have been wild and wayward, but you'll forgive
    me now ;
You'll kiss me, my own mother, and forgive me
    ere I go ;

Nay, nay, you must not weep, nor let your grief
    be wild,
You should not fret for me, mother, you have
    another child.

If I can I'll come again, mother, from out my
    resting-place;
Tho' you'll not see me, mother, I shall look upon
    your face;
Tho' I cannot speak a word, I shall harken what
    you say,
And be often, often with you when you think I'm
    far away.

Goodnight, goodnight, when I have said goodnight
    for evermore,
And you see me carried out from the threshold of
    the door;
Don't let Effie come to see me till my grave be
    growing green:
She'll be a better child to you than ever I have
    been.

She'll find my garden-tools upon the granary
    floor:
Let her take 'em: they are hers: I shall never
    garden more:
But tell her, when I'm gone, to train the rose-bush
    that I set
About the parlour-window and the box of
    mignonette.

Good-night, sweet mother : call me before the day
    is born.
All night I lie awake, but I fall asleep at
    morn ;
But I would see the sun rise upon the glad New-
    year,
So, if you're waking, call me, call me early, mother
    dear.

CONCLUSION.

I THOUGHT to pass away before, and yet alive
    I am ;
And in the fields all round I hear the bleating of
    the lamb.
How sadly, I remember, rose the morning of the
    year !
To die before the snowdrop came, and now the
    violet's here.

O sweet is the new violet, that comes beneath the
    skies,
And sweeter is the young lamb's voice to me that
    cannot rise,
And sweet is all the land about, and all the flowers
    that blow,
And sweeter far is death than life to me that long
    to go.

It seem'd so hard at first, mother, to leave the
    blessed sun,
And now it seems as hard to stay, and yet His will
    be done !

But still I think it can't be long before I find
    release ;
And that good man, the clergyman, has told me
    words of peace.

O blessings on his kindly voice and on his silver
    hair !
And blessings on his whole life long, until he meet
    me there !
O blessings on his kindly heart and on his silver
    head !
A thousand times I blest him, as he knelt beside
    my bed.

He taught me all the mercy, for he show'd me all
    the sin.
Now, tho' my lamp was lighted late, there's One
    will let me in :
Nor would I now be well, mother, again, if that
    could be,
For my desire is but to pass to Him that died
    for me.

I did not hear the dog howl, mother, or the death-
    watch beat,
There came a sweeter token when the night and
    morning meet :
But sit beside my bed, mother, and put your hand
    in mine,
And Effie on the other side, and I will tell the
    sign.

All in the wild March-morning I heard the angels
    call ;
It was when the moon was setting, and the dark was
    over all ;
The trees began to whisper, and the wind began
    to roll,
And in the wild March-morning I heard them call
    my soul.

For lying broad awake I thought of you and Effie
    dear ;
I saw you sitting in the house, and I no longer
    here ;
With all my strength I pray'd for both, and so I
    felt resign'd,
And up the valley came a swell of music on the
    wind.

I thought that it was fancy, and I listen'd in
    my bed,
And then did something speak to me—I know not
    what was said ;
For great delight and shuddering took hold of all
    my mind,
And up the valley came again the music on the
    wind.

But you were sleeping ; and I said, "It's not for
    them : it's mine."
And if it comes three times, I thought, I take it
    for a sign.

And once again it came, and close beside the
    window-bars,
Then seem'd to go right up to Heaven and die
    among the stars.

So now I think my time is near. I trust it is. I
    know
The blessed music went that way my soul will have
    to go.
And for myself, indeed, I care not if I go
    to-day.
But, Effie, you must comfort *her* when I am past
    away.

And say to Robin a kind word, and tell him not
    to fret ;
There's many worthier than I, would make him
    happy yet.
If I had lived—I cannot tell—I might have been
    his wife ;
But all these things have ceased to be, with my
    desire of life.

O look ! the sun begins to rise, the heavens are in
    a glow ;
He shines upon a hundred fields, and all of them I
    know.
And there I move no longer now, and there his
    light may shine—
Wild flowers in the valley for other hands than
    mine.

O sweet and strange it seems to me, that ere this
    day is done
The voice, that now is speaking, may be beyond
    the sun—
For ever and for ever with those just souls and
    true—
And what is life, that we should moan ? why make
    we such ado ?

For ever and for ever, all in a blessed
    home—
And there to wait a little while till you and Effie
    come—
To lie within the light of God, as I lie upon your
    breast—
And the wicked cease from troubling, and the weary
    are at rest.

DORA.

WITH farmer Allan at the farm abode
William and Dora.   William was his son,
And she his niece.   He often look'd at them,
And often thought " I'll make them man and wife."

Now Dora felt her uncle's will in all,
And yearn'd towards William ; but the youth, because
He had been always with her in the house,
Thought not of Dora.   Then there came a day
When Allan call'd his son, and said, " My son :
I married late, but I would wish to see
My grandchild on my knees before I die :
And I have set my heart upon a match.

Now therefore look to Dora ; she is well
To look to ; thrifty too beyond her age.
She is my brother's daughter : he and I
Had once hard words, and parted, and he died
In foreign lands ; but for his sake I bred
His daughter Dora : take her for your wife ;
For I have wish'd this marriage, night and day,
For many years."   But William answer'd short ;
" I cannot marry Dora ; by my life,
I will not marry Dora."

       Then the old man
Was wroth, and doubled up his hands, and said ;
" You will not, boy ! you dare to answer thus !
But in my time a father's word was law,
And so it shall be now for me.   Look to it ;
Consider, William : take a month to think,
And let me have an answer to my wish ;
Or, by the Lord that made me, you shall pack,
And never more darken my doors again."
But William answer'd madly ; bit his lips,
And broke away.   The more he look'd at her
The less he liked her ; and his ways were harsh ;
But Dora bore them meekly.   Then before
The month was out he left his father's house,
And hired himself to work within the fields ;
And half in love, half spite, he woo'd and wed
A labourer's daughter, Mary Morrison.

  Then, when the bells were ringing, Allan call'd
His niece and said : " My girl, I love you well ;
But if you speak with him that was my son,
Or change a word with her he calls his wife,
My home is none of yours.   My will is law."

And Dora promised, being meek.   She thought,
"It cannot be : my uncle's mind will change !"

   And days went on, and there was born a boy
To William ; then distresses came on him ;
And day by day he pass'd his father's gate,
Heart-broken, and his father help'd him not.
But Dora stored what little she could save,
And sent it them by stealth, nor did they know
Who sent it ; till at last a fever seized
On William, and in harvest time he died.

   Then Dora went to Mary.   Mary sat
And look'd with tears upon her boy, and thought
Hard things of Dora.   Dora came and said :
"I have obey'd my uncle until now,
And I have sinn'd, for it was all thro' me
This evil came on William at the first.
But, Mary, for the sake of him that's gone,
And for your sake, the woman that he chose,
And for this orphan, I am come to you :
You know there has not been for these five years
So full a harvest : let me take the boy,
And I will set him in my uncle's eye
Among the wheat ; that when his heart is glad
Of the full harvest, he may see the boy,
And bless him for the sake of him that's gone."

   And Dora took the child, and went her way
Across the wheat, and sat upon a mound
That was unsown, where many poppies grew.
Far off the farmer came into the field
And spied her not ; for none of all his men
Dare tell him Dora waited with the child ;
And Dora would have risen and gone to him,

But her heart fail'd her ; and the reapers reap'd,
And the sun fell, and all the land was dark.

But when the morrow came, she rose and took
The child once more, and sat upon the mound;
And made a little wreath of all the flowers
That grew about, and tied it round his hat
To make him pleasing in her uncle's eye.
Then when the farmer pass'd into the field
He spied her, and he left his men at work,
And came and said ; " Where were you yesterday ?
Whose child is that ? What are you doing here ? "
So Dora cast her eyes upon the ground,
And answer'd softly, " This is William's child ! "
" And did I not," said Allan, " did I not
Forbid you, Dora ? " Dora said again ;
" Do with me as you will, but take the child
And bless him for the sake of him that's gone ! "
And Allan said, " I see it is a trick
Got up betwixt you and the woman there.
I must be taught my duty, and by you !
You knew my word was law, and yet you dared
To slight it. Well—for I will take the boy ;
But go you hence, and never see me more."

So saying, he took the boy, that cried aloud
And struggled hard. The wreath of flowers fell
At Dora's feet. She bow'd upon her hands,
And the boy's cry came to her from the field,
More and more distant. She bow'd down her head,
Remembering the day when first she came,
And all the things that had been. She bow'd down
And wept in secret ; and the reapers reap'd,
And the sun fell, and all the land was dark.

Then Dora went to Mary's house, and stood
Upon the threshold.   Mary saw the boy
Was not with Dora.   She broke out in praise
To God, that help'd her in her widowhood.
And Dora said, " My uncle took the boy ;
But, Mary, let me live and work with you :
He says that he will never see me more."
Then answer'd Mary, "This shall never be,
That thou shouldst take my trouble on thyself :
And, now I think, he shall not have the boy,
For he will teach him hardness, and to slight
His mother ; therefore thou and I will go,
And I will have my boy, and bring him home ;
And I will beg of him to take thee back ;
But if he will not take thee back again,
Then thou and I will live within one house,
And work for William's child, until he grows
Of age to help us."
              So the women kiss'd
Each other, and set out, and reach'd the farm.
The door was off the latch : they peep'd, and saw
The boy set up betwixt his grandsire's knees,
Who thrust him in the hollows of his arm,
And clapt him on the hands, and on the cheeks,
Like one that loved him ; and the lad stretch'd out
And babbled for the golden seal, that hung
From Allan's watch, and sparkled by the fire.
Then they came in : but when the boy beheld
His mother, he cried out to come to her :
And Allan set him down, and Mary said :

    " O Father !—if you let me call you so—
I never came a-begging for myself,
Or William, or this child ; but now I come

For Dora : take her back ; she loves you well.
O Sir, when William died, he died at peace
With all men ; for I ask'd him, and he said,
He could not ever rue his marrying me—
I had been a patient wife : but, Sir, he said
That he was wrong to cross his father thus :
'God bless him !' he said, 'and may he never know
The troubles I have gone thro' !'   Then he turn'd
His face and pass'd—unhappy that I am !
But now, Sir, let me have my boy, for you
Will make him hard, and he will learn to slight
His father's memory ; and take Dora back,
And let all this be as it was before."

So Mary said, and Dora hid her face
By Mary.   There was silence in the room ;
And all at once the old man burst in sobs :—
  "I have been to blame—to blame.   I have kill'd
        my son.
I have kill'd him—but I loved him—my dear son.
May God forgive me !—I have been to blame.
Kiss me, my children."
                            Then they clung about
The old man's neck, and kiss'd him many times.
And all the man was broken with remorse ;
And all his love came back a hundredfold ;
And for three hours he sobb'd o'er William's child,
Thinking of William.
                            So those four abode
Within one house together ; and as years
Went forward, Mary took another mate ;
But Dora lived unmarried till her death.

THE BROOK.

AN IDYL.

" HERE, by this brook, we parted ; I to the East
And he for Italy—too late—too late :
One whom the strong sons of the world despise ;
For lucky rhymes to him were scrip and share,
And mellow metres more than cent for cent ;
Nor could he understand how money breeds,
Thought it a dead thing ; yet himself could make
The thing that is not as the thing that is.
O had he lived !   In our schoolbooks we say,
Of those that held their heads above the crowd,
They flourish'd then or then ; but life in him
Could scarce be said to flourish, only touch'd
On such a time as goes before the leaf,
When all the wood stands in a mist of green,
And nothing perfect : yet the brook he loved,
For which, in branding summers of Bengal,
Or ev'n the sweet half-English Neilgherry air,
I panted, seems, as I re-listen to it,
Prattling the primrose fancies of the boy,
To me that loved him ; for 'O brook,' he says,
'O babbling brook,' says Edmund in his rhyme,
'Whence come you ?' and the brook, why not ? replies.

        I come from haunts of coot and hern,
            I make a sudden sally
        And sparkle out among the fern,
            To bicker down a valley.

        By thirty hills I hurry down,
            Or slip between the ridges,
        By twenty thorps, a little town,
            And half a hundred bridges.

Till last by Philip's farm I flow
  To join the brimming river,
For men may come and men may go,
  But I go on for ever.

" Poor lad, he died at Florence, quite worn out,
Travelling to Naples.   There is Darnley bridge,
It has more ivy ; there the river ; and there
Stands Philip's farm where brook and river meet.

I chatter over stony ways,
  In little sharps and trebles,
I bubble into eddying bays,
  I babble on the pebbles.

With many a curve my banks I fret
  By many a field and fallow,
And many a fairy foreland set
  With willow-weed and mallow.

I chatter, chatter, as I flow
  To join the brimming river,
For men may come and men may go,
  But I go on for ever.

" But Philip chatter'd more than brook or bird ;
Old Philip ; all about the fields you caught
His weary daylong chirping, like the dry
High-elbow'd grigs that leap in summer grass.

I wind about, and in and out,
  With here a blossom sailing,
And here and there a lusty trout,
  And here and there a grayling.

And here and there a foamy flake
  Upon me, as I travel
With many a silvery waterbreak
  Above the golden gravel.

And draw them all along, and flow
  To join the brimming river,
For men may come and men may go,
  But I go on for ever.

" O darling Katie Willows, his one child !
A maiden of our century, yet most meek ;
A daughter of our meadows, yet not coarse ;
Straight, but as lissome as a hazel wand ;
Her eyes a bashful azure, and her hair
In gloss and hue the chestnut, when the shell
Divides threefold to show the fruit within.

" Sweet Katie, once I did her a good turn,
Her and her far-off cousin and betrothed,
James Willows, of one name and heart with her.
For here I came, twenty-years back—the week
Before I parted with poor Edmund ; crost
By that old bridge which, half in ruins then,
Still makes a hoary eyebrow for the gleam
Beyond it, where the waters marry—crost,
Whistling a random bar of Bonny Doon,
And push'd at Philip's garden-gate.   The gate,
Half-parted from a weak and scolding hinge,
Stuck ; and he clamour'd from a casement, 'run'
To Katie somewhere in the walks below,
'Run, Katie !' Katie never ran : she moved
To meet me, winding under woodbine bowers,
A little flutter'd, with her eyelids down,
Fresh apple-blossom, blushing for a boon.

" What was it ? less of sentiment than sense
Had Katie ; not illiterate ; neither one
Who dabbling in the fount of fictive tears,
And nursed by mealy-mouth'd philanthropies,
Divorce the Feeling from her mate the Deed.

"She told me.   She and James had quarrell'd.   Why ?
What cause of quarrel?   None, she said, no cause ;

James had no cause : but when I prest the cause,
I learnt that James had flickering jealousies
Which anger'd her.　Who anger'd James? I said.
But Katie snatch'd her eyes at once from mine,
And sketching with her slender pointed foot
Some figure like a wizard's pentagram
On garden gravel, let my query pass
Unclaim'd, in flushing silence, till I ask'd
If James were coming.　'Coming every day,'
She answer'd, 'ever longing to explain,
But evermore her father came across
With some long-winded tale, and broke him short ;
And James departed vext with him and her.'
How could I help her ?　'Would I—was it wrong?'
(Claspt hands and that petitionary grace
Of sweet seventeen subdued me ere she spoke)
'O would I take her father for one hour,
For one half-hour, and let him talk to me !'
And even while she spoke, I saw where James
Made toward us, like a wader in the surf,
Beyond the brook, waist-deep in meadow-sweet.

　　"O Katie, what I suffer'd for your sake !
For in I went, and call'd old Philip out
To show the farm : full willingly he rose :
He led me thro' the short sweet-smelling lanes
Of his wheat-suburb, babbling as he went.
He praised his land, his horses, his machines ;
He praised his ploughs, his cows, his hogs, his dogs ;
He praised his hens, his geese, his guinea-hens ;
His pigeons, who in session on their roofs
Approved him, bowing at their own deserts ;
Then from the plaintive mother's teat he took

Her blind and shuddering puppies, naming each,
And naming those, his friends, for whom they were :
Then crost the common into Darnley chase
To show Sir Arthur's deer.   In copse and fern
Twinkled the innumerable ear and tail.
Then, seated on a serpent-rooted beech,
He pointed out a pasturing colt, and said :
' That was the four-year-old I sold the Squire.'
And there he told a long long-winded tale
Of how the Squire had seen the colt at grass,
And how it was the thing his daughter wish'd,
And how he sent the bailiff to the farm
To learn the price, and what the price he ask'd,
And how the bailiff swore that he was mad,
But he stood firm ; and so the matter hung ;
He gave them line : and five days after that
He met the bailiff at the Golden Fleece,
Who then and there had offer'd something more,
But he stood firm ; and so the matter hung ;
He knew the man ; the colt would fetch its price ;
He gave them line : and how by chance at last
(It might be May or April, he forgot,
The last of April or the first of May)
He found the bailiff riding by the farm,
And, talking from the point, he drew him in,
And there he mellow'd all his heart with ale,
Until they closed a bargain, hand in hand.

   "Then, while I breathed in sight of haven, he,
Poor fellow, could he help it ? recommenced,
And ran thro' all the coltish chronicle,
Wild Will, Black Bess, Tantivy, Tallyho,
Reform, White Rose, Bellerophon, the Jilt,
Arbaces, and Phenomenon, and the rest,

Till, not to die a listener, I arose,
And with me Philip, talking still ; and so
We turn'd our foreheads from the falling sun,
And following our own shadows thrice as long
As when they follow'd us from Philip's door,
Arrived, and found the sun of sweet content
Re-risen in Katie's eyes, and all things well.

I steal by lawns and grassy plots,
I slide by hazel covers ;
I move the sweet forget-me-nots
That grow for happy lovers.

I slip, I slide, I gloom, I glance,
Among my skimming swallows ;
I make the netted sunbeam dance
Against my sandy shallows.

I murmur under moon and stars
In brambly wildernesses ;
I linger by my shingly bars ;
I loiter round my cresses ;

And out again I curve and flow
To join the brimming river,
For men may come and men may go,
But I go on for ever.

Yes, men may come and go ; and these are gone,
All gone.   My dearest brother, Edmund, sleeps,
Not by the well-known stream and rustic spire,
But unfamiliar Arno, and the dome
Of Brunelleschi ; sleeps in peace : and he,
Poor Philip, of all his lavish waste of words
Remains the lean P. W. on his tomb :
I scraped the lichen from it : Katie walks
By the long wash of Australasian seas
Far off, and holds her head to other stars,
And breathes in converse seasons.   All are gone."

So Lawrence Aylmer, seated on a stile
In the long hedge, and rolling in his mind
Old waifs of rhyme, and bowing o'er the brook
A tonsuréd head in middle age forlorn,
Mused, and was mute.   On a sudden a low breath
Of tender air made tremble in the hedge
The fragile bindweed-bells and briony rings ;
And he look'd up.   There stood a maiden near,
Waiting to pass.   In much amaze he stared
On eyes a bashful azure, and on hair
In gloss and hue the chestnut, when the shell
Divides threefold to show the fruit within :
Then, wondering, ask'd her " Are you from the farm ? "
"Yes," answer'd she.   "Pray stay a little : pardon me ;
What do they call you ? " "Katie." "That were strange.
What surname ? " "Willows." "No ! " "That is my name."
" Indeed ! " and here he look'd so self-perplext,
That Katie laugh'd, and laughing blush'd, till he
Laugh'd also, but as one before he wakes,
Who feels a glimmering strangeness in his dream.
Then looking at her ; " Too happy, fresh and fair,
Too fresh and fair in our sad world's best bloom,
To be the ghost of one who bore your name
About these meadows, twenty years ago."

" Have you not heard ? " said Katie, " we came back.
We bought the farm we tenanted before.
Am I so like her? so they said on board.
Sir, if you knew her in her English days,
My mother, as it seems you did, the days
That most she loves to talk of, come with me.
My brother James is in the harvest-field :
But she—you will be welcome—O, come in ! "

THE TALKING OAK

ONCE more the gate behind me falls ;
　　Once more before my face
I see the moulder'd Abbey-walls,
　　That stand within the chace.

Beyond the lodge the city lies,
　　Beneath its drift of smoke ;
And ah ! with what delighted eyes
　　I turn to yonder oak.

For when my passion first began,
　　Ere that, which in me burn'd,
The love, that makes me thrice a man
　　Could hope itself return'd ;

To yonder oak within the field
　　I spoke without restraint,
And with a larger faith appeal'd
　　Than Papist unto Saint.

For oft I talked with him apart,
　　And told him of my choice,
Until he plagiarised a heart,
　　And answer'd with a voice.

Tho' what he whisper'd under Heaven
　　None else could understand ;
I found him garrulously given,
　　A babbler in the land.

But since I heard him make reply
    Is many a weary hour ;
'Twere well to question him, and try,
    If yet he keeps the power.

Hail, hidden to the knees in fern,
    Broad Oak of Sumner-chace,
Whose topmost branches can discern
    The roofs of Sumner-place !

Say thou, whereon I carved her name,
    If ever maid or spouse,
As fair as my Olivia, came
    To rest beneath thy boughs.—

" O Walter, I have shelter'd here
    Whatever maiden grace
The good old Summers, year by year,
    Made ripe in Sumner-chace :

" Old Summers, when the monk was fat,
    And, issuing shorn and sleek,
Would twist his girdle tight, and pat
    The girls upon the cheek,

" Ere yet, in scorn of Peter's-pence,
    And number'd bead, and shrift,
Bluff Harry broke into the spence,
    And turn'd the cowls adrift :

" And I have seen some score of those
    Fresh faces, that would thrive
When his man-minded offset rose
    To chase the deer at five ;

4

" And all that from the town would stroll,
    Till that wild wind made work
In which the gloomy brewer's soul
    Went by me, like a stork:

" The slight she-slips of loyal blood,
    And others, passing praise,
Strait-laced, but all-too-full in bud
    For puritanic stays:

" And I have shadow'd many a group
    Of beauties, that were born
In teacup-times of hood and hoop,
    Or while the patch was worn;

" And, leg and arm with love-knots gay,
    About me leap'd and laugh d
The modish Cupid of the day,
    And shrill'd his tinsel shaft.

" I swear (and else may insects prick
    Each leaf into a gall)
This girl, for whom your heart is sick,
    Is three times worth them all;

" For those and theirs, by Nature's law,
    Have faded long ago;
But in these latter springs I saw
    Your own Olivia blow,

" From when she gamboll'd on the greens,
    A baby-germ, to when
The maiden blossoms of her teens
    Could number five from ten.

" I swear, by leaf, and wind, and rain,
 (And hear me with thine ears,)
That, tho' I circle in the grain
 Five hundred rings of years.——

" Yet, since I first could cast a shade,
 Did never creature pass
So slightly, musically made,
 So light upon the grass :

" For as to fairies, that will flit
 To make the greensward fresh,
I hold them exquisitely knit,
 But far too spare of flesh."

Oh, hide thy knotted knees in fern,
 And overlook the chace ;
And from thy topmost branch discern
 The roofs of Sumner-place.

But thou, whereon I carved her name,
 That oft hast heard my vows,
Declare when last Olivia came
 To sport beneath thy boughs.

" O yesterday, you know, the fair
 Was holden at the town ;
Her father left his good arm-chair,
 And rode his hunter down.

" And with him Albert came on his.
 I look'd at him with joy :
As cowslip unto oxlip is,
 So seems she to the boy.

" An hour had past—and, sitting straight
    Within the low-wheel'd chaise,
Her mother trundled to the gate
    Behind the dappled grays.

" But, as for her, she stay'd at home,
    And on the roof she went,
And down the way you used to come,
    She look'd with discontent.

" She left the novel half-uncut
    Upon the rosewood shelf ;
She left the new piano shut :
    She could not please herself.

" Then ran she, gamesome as the colt,
    And livelier than a lark
She sent her voice thro' all the holt
    Before her, and the park.

" A light wind chased her on the wing,
    And in the chase grew wild,
As close as might be would he cling
    About the darling child :

" But light as any wind that blows
    So fleetly did she stir,
The flower, she touch'd on, dipt and rose,
    And turn'd to look at her.

" And here she came, and round me play'd,
    And sang to me the whole
Of those three stanzas that you made
    About my ' giant bole ; '

" And in a fit of frolic mirth
    She strove to span my waist :
Alas, I was so broad of girth,
    I could not be embraced.

" I wish'd myself the fair young beech
    That here beside me stands,
That round me, clasping each in each,
    She might have lock'd her hands.

" Yet seem'd the pressure thrice as sweet
    As woodbine's fragile hold,
Or when I feel about my feet
    The berried briony fold."

O muffle round thy knees with fern,
    And shadow Sumner-chace !
Long may thy topmost branch discern
    The roofs of Sumner-place !

But tell me, did she read the name
    I carved with many vows
When last with throbbing heart I came
    To rest beneath thy boughs ?

" O yes, she wander'd round and round
    These knotted knees of mine,
And found, and kiss'd the name she found
    And sweetly murmur'd thine.

" A teardrop trembled from its source,
    And down my surface crept.
My sense of touch is something coarse.
    But I believe she wept.

" Then flush'd her cheek with rosy light,
    She glanced across the plain ;
But not a creature was in sight:
    She kiss'd me once again.

" Her kisses were so close and kind,
    That, trust me on my word,
Hard wood I am, and wrinkled rind,
    But yet my sap was stirr'd :

" And even into my inmost ring
    A pleasure I discern'd,
Like those blind motions of the Spring,
    That show the year is turn'd.

" Thrice-happy he that may caress
    The ringlet's waving balm—
The cushions of whose touch may press
    The maiden's tender palm.

" I, rooted here among the groves,
    But languidly adjust
My vapid vegetable loves
    With anthers and with dust :

" For ah ! my friend, the days were brief
    Whereof the poets talk,
When that, which breathes within the leaf,
    Could slip its bark and walk.

" But could I, as in times foregone,
    From spray, and branch, and stem,
Have suck'd and gather'd into one
    The life that spreads in them,

" She had not found me so remiss ;
 But lightly issuing thro',
I would have paid her kiss for kiss,
 With usury thereto."

O flourish high, with leafy towers,
 And overlook the lea,
Pursue thy loves among the bowers,
 But leave thou mine to me.

O flourish, hidden deep in fern,
 Old oak, I love thee well ;
A thousand thanks for what I learn
 And what remains to tell.

" 'Tis little more : the day was warm ;
 At last, tired out with play,
She sank her head upon her arm,
 And at my feet she lay.

" Her eyelids dropp'd their silken eaves.
 I breathed upon her eyes
Thro' all the summer of my leaves
 A welcome mix'd with sighs.

" I took the swarming sound of life—
 The music from the town—
The murmurs of the drum and fife
 And lull'd them in my own.

" Sometimes I let a sunbeam slip,
 To light her shaded eye ;
A second flutter'd round her lip
 Like a golden butterfly ;

" A third would glimmer on her neck
  To make the necklace shine ;
Another slid, a sunny fleck,
  From head to ancle fine.

" Then close and dark my arms I spread,
  And shadow'd all her rest—
Dropt dews upon her golden head,
  An acorn in her breast.

" But in a pet she started up,
  And pluck'd it out, and drew
My little oakling from the cup,
  And flung him in the dew.

" And yet it was a graceful gift—
  I felt a pang within
As when I see the woodman lift
  His axe to slay my kin.

" I shook him down because he was
  The finest on the tree.
He lies beside thee on the grass.
  O kiss him once for me.

" O kiss him twice and thrice for me,
  That have no lips to kiss,
For never yet was oak on lea
  Shall grow so fair as this."

Step deeper yet in herb and fern,
  Look further thro' the chace,
Spread upward till thy boughs discern
  The front of Sumner-place.

This fruit of thine by Love is blest,
    That but a moment lay
Where fairer fruit of Love may rest
    Some happy future day.

I kiss it twice, I kiss it thrice,
    The warmth it thence shall win
To riper life may magnetise
    The baby-oak within.

But thou, while kingdoms overset,
    Or lapse from hand to hand,
Thy leaf shall never fail, nor yet
    Thine acorn in the land.

May never saw dismember thee,
    Nor wielded axe disjoint,
That art the fairest-spoken tree
    From here to Lizard-point.

O rock upon thy towery top
    All throats that gurgle sweet!
All starry culmination drop
    Balm-dews to bathe thy feet!

All grass of silky feather grow—
    And while he sinks or swells
The full south-breeze around thee blow
    The sound of minster bells.

The fat earth feed thy branchy root,
    That under deeply strikes!
The northern morning o'er thee shoot,
    High up, in silver spikes!

Nor ever lightning char thy grain,
    But, rolling as in sleep,
Low thunders bring the mellow rain,
    That makes thee broad and deep !

And hear me swear a solemn oath,
    That only by thy side
Will I to Olive plight my troth,
    And gain her for my bride.

And when my marriage morn may fall,
    She, Dryad-like, shall wear
Alternate leaf and acorn-ball
    In wreath about her hair.

And I will work in prose and rhyme,
    And praise thee more in both
Than bard has honour'd beech or lime,
    Or that Thessalian growth,

In which the swarthy ringdove sat,
    And mystic sentence spoke ;
And more than England honours that,
    Thy famous brother-oak,

Wherein the younger Charles abode
    Till all the paths were dim,
And far below the Roundhead rode,
    And humm'd a surly hymn.

THE GARDENER'S DAUGHTER ; OR,
THE PICTURES.

THIS morning is the morning of the day,
When I and Eustace from the city went
To see the Gardener's Daughter ; I and he,
Brothers in Art ; a friendship so complete
Portion'd in halves between us, that we grew
The fable of the city where we dwelt.

    My Eustace might have sat for Hercules ;
So muscular he spread, so broad of breast.
He, by some law that holds in love, and draws
The greater to the lesser, long desired
A certain miracle of symmetry,
A miniature of loveliness, all grace
Summ'd up and closed in little ;—Juliet, she
So light of foot, so light of spirit—oh, she
To me myself, for some three careless moons,
The summer pilot of an empty heart
Unto the shores of nothing !   Know you not
Such touches are but embassies of love,
To tamper with the feelings, ere he found
Empire for life ? but Eustace painted her,
And said to me, she sitting with us then,
" When will *you* paint like this ? " and I replied,
(My words were half in earnest, half in jest),
" 'Tis not your work, but Love's.   Love, unper-
    ceived,
A more ideal Artist he than all,
Came, drew your pencil from you, made those eyes
Darker than darkest pansies, and that hair

More black than ashbuds in the front of March."
And Juliet answer'd laughing, " Go and see
The Gardener's daughter : trust me, after that,
You scarce can fail to match his masterpiece."
And up we rose, and on the spur we went.

   Not wholly in the busy world, nor quite
Beyond it, blooms the garden that I love.
News from the humming city comes to it
In sound of funeral or of marriage bells ;
And, sitting muffled in dark leaves, you hear
The windy clanging of the minster clock ;
Although between it and the garden lies
A league of grass, wash'd by a slow broad stream,
That, stirr'd with languid pulses of the oar,
Waves all its lazy lilies, and creeps on,
Barge-laden, to three arches of a bridge
Crown'd with the minster-towers.

                      The fields between
Are dewy-fresh, browsed by deep-udder'd kine,
And all about the large lime feathers low,
The lime a summer home of murmurous wings.

   In that still place she, hoarded in herself,
Grew, seldom seen : not less among us lived
Her fame from lip to lip.   Who had not heard
Of Rose, the Gardener's daughter ?   Where was he,
So blunt in memory, so old at heart,
At such a distance from his youth in grief,
That, having seen, forgot ?   The common mouth,
So gross to express delight, in praise of her
Grew oratory.   Such a lord is Love,
And Beauty such a mistress of the world.

And if I said that Fancy, led by Love,
Would play with flying forms and images,
Yet this is also true, that, long before
I look'd upon her, when I heard her name
My heart was like a prophet to my heart,
And told me I should love.   A crowd of hopes,
That sought to sow themselves like winged seeds,
Born out of everything I heard and saw,
Flutter'd about my senses and my soul ;
And vague desires, like fitful blasts of balm
To one that travels quickly, made the air
Of Life delicious, and all kinds of thought
That verged upon them, sweeter than the dream
Dream'd by a happy man, when the dark East,
Unseen, is brightening to his bridal morn.

   And sure this orbit of the memory folds
For ever in itself the day we went
To see her.   All the land in flowery squares,
Beneath a broad and equal-blowing wind,
Smelt of the coming summer, as one large cloud
Drew downward : but all else of Heaven was pure
Up to the Sun, and May from verge to verge,
And May with me from head to heel.   And now,
As tho' 'twere yesterday, as tho' it were
The hour just flown, that morn with all its sound,
(For those old Mays had thrice the life of these,)
Rings in mine ears.   The steer forgot to graze,
And, where the hedge-row cuts the pathway, stood,
Leaning his horns into the neighbour field,
And lowing to his fellows.   From the woods
Came voices of the well-contented doves.
The lark could scarce get out his notes for joy,

But shook his song together as he near'd
His happy home, the ground. To left and right,
The cuckoo told his name to all the hills ;
The mellow ouzel fluted in the elm ;
The redcap whistled ; and the nightingale
Sang loud, as tho' he were the bird of day.

   And Eustace turn'd, and smiling said to me,
" Hear how the bushes echo ! by my life,
These birds have joyful thoughts. Think you they sing
Like poets, from the vanity of song ?
Or have they any sense of why they sing ?
And would they praise the heavens for what they have ? "
And I made answer, " Were there nothing else
For which to praise the heavens but only love,
That only love were cause enough for praise."

   Lightly he laugh'd, as one that read my thought,
And on we went ; but ere an hour had pass'd,
We reach'd a meadow slanting to the North ;
Down which a well-worn pathway courted us
To one green wicket in a privet hedge ;
This, yielding, gave into a grassy walk
Thro' crowded lilac-ambush trimly pruned ;
And one warm gust, full-fed with perfume, blew
Beyond us, as we enter'd in the cool.
The garden stretches southward. In the midst
A cedar spread his dark-green layers of shade.
The garden-glasses shone, and momently
The twinkling laurel scatter'd silver lights.
   "Eustace," I said, "This wonder keeps the house."
He nodded, but a moment afterwards
He cried, " Look ! look ! " Before he ceased I turn'd,
And, ere a star can wink, beheld her there.

For up the porch there grew an Eastern rose,
That, flowering high, the last night's gale had caught,
And blown across the walk.   One arm aloft—
Gown'd in pure white, that fitted to the shape—
Holding the bush, to fix it back, she stood.
A single stream of all her soft brown hair
Pour'd on one side : the shadow of the flowers
Stole all the golden gloss, and, wavering
Lovingly lower, trembled on her waist—
Ah, happy shade—and still went wavering down,
But, ere it touch'd a foot, that might have danced
The greensward into greener circles, dipt,
And mix'd with shadows of the common ground !
But the full day dwelt on her brows, and sunn'd
Her violet eyes, and all her Hebe-bloom,
And doubled his own warmth against her lips,
And on the bounteous wave of such a breast
As never pencil drew.   Half light, half shade,
She stood, a sight to make an old man young.

So rapt, we neared the house ; but she, a Rose
In roses, mingled with her fragrant toil,
Nor heard us come, nor from her tendance turn'd
Into the world without ; till close at hand,
And almost ere I knew mine own intent,
This murmur broke the stillness of that air
Which brooded round about her :
                              "Ah, one rose,
One rose, but one, by those fair fingers cull'd,
Were worth a hundred kisses press'd on lips
Less exquisite than thine."
                              She look'd : but all
Suffused with blushes—neither self-possess'd

Nor startled, but betwixt this mood and that,
Divided in a graceful quiet—paused,
And dropt the branch she held, and turning, wound
Her looser hair in braid, and stirr'd her lips
For some sweet answer, tho' no answer came,
Nor yet refused the rose, but granted it,
And moved away, and left me, statue-like,
In act to render thanks.

                        I, that whole day,
Saw her no more, altho' I linger'd there
Till every daisy slept, and Love's white star
Beam'd thro' the thicken'd cedar in the dusk.

So home we went, and all the livelong way
With solemn gibe did Eustace banter me.
"Now," said he, "will you climb the top of Art.
You cannot fail but work in hues to dim
The Titianic Flora.   Will you match
My Juliet? you, not you,—the Master, Love,
A more ideal Artist he than all."

So home I went, but could not sleep for joy,
Reading her perfect features in the gloom,
Kissing the rose she gave me o'er and o'er,
And shaping faithful record of the glance
That graced the giving—such a noise of life
Swarm'd in the golden present, such a voice
Call'd to me from the years to come, and such
A length of bright horizon rimm'd the dark.
And all that night I heard the watchmen peal
The sliding season : all that night I heard
The heavy clocks knolling the drowsy hours.
The drowsy hours, dispensers of all good,

O'er the mute city stole with folded wings,
Distilling odours on me as they went
To greet their fairer sisters of the East.

Love at first sight, first-born, and heir to all,
Made this night thus.   Henceforward squall nor storm
Could keep me from that Eden where she dwelt.
Light pretexts drew me : sometimes a Dutch love
For tulips ; then for roses, moss or musk,
To grace my city-rooms ; or fruits and cream
Served in the weeping elm ; and more and more
A word could bring the colour to my cheek ;
A thought would fill my eyes with happy dew ;
Love trebled life within me, and with each
The year increased.
                    The daughters of the year,
One after one, thro' that still garden pass'd :
Each garlanded with her peculiar flower
Danced into light, and died into the shade ;
And each in passing touch'd with some new grace
Or seem'd to touch her, so that day by day,
Like one that never can be wholly known,
Her beauty grew ; till Autumn brought an hour
For Eustace, when I heard his deep " I will,"
Breathed, like the covenant of a God, to hold
From thence thro' all the worlds : but I rose up
Full of his bliss, and following her dark eyes
Felt earth as air beneath me, till I reach'd
The wicket-gate, and found her standing there.

There sat we down upon a garden mound,
Two mutually enfolded ; Love, the third,
Between us, in the circle of his arms

Enwound us both ; and over many a range
Of waning lime the gray cathedral towers,
Across a hazy glimmer of the west,
Reveal'd their shining windows : from them clash'd
The bells ; we listen'd ; with the time we play'd ;
We spoke of other things ; we coursed about
The subject most at heart, more near and near,
Like doves about a dovecote, wheeling round
The central wish, until we settled there.

Then, in that time and place, I spoke to her,
Requiring, tho' I knew it was mine own,
Yet for the pleasure that I took to hear,
Requiring at her hand the greatest gift,
A woman's heart, the heart of her I loved ;
And in that time and place she answer'd me,
And in the compass of three little words,
More musical than ever came in one,
The silver fragments of a broken voice,
Made me most happy, faltering " I am thine."

Shall I cease here ?   Is this enough to say
That my desire, like all strongest hopes,
By its own energy fulfill'd itself,
Merged in completion ?   Would you learn at full
How passion rose thro' circumstantial grades
Beyond all grades develop'd ? and indeed
I had not staid so long to tell you all,
But while I mused came Memory with sad eyes,
Holding the folded annals of my youth ;
And while I mused, Love with knit brows went by,
And with a flying finger swept my lips,
And spake, " Be wise : not easily forgiven

Are those, who setting wide the doors, that bar
The secret bridal chambers of the heart,
Let in the day."   Here, then, my words have end.

· Yet might I tell of meetings, of farewells—
Of that which came between, more sweet than each,
In whispers, like the whispers of the leaves
That tremble round a nightingale—in sighs
Which perfect Joy, perplex'd for utterance,
Stole from her sister Sorrow.   Might I not tell
Of difference, reconcilement, pledges given,
And vows, where there was never need of vows,
And kisses, where the heart on one wild leap
Hung tranced from all pulsation, as above
The heavens between their fairy fleeces pale
Sow'd all their mystic gulfs with fleeting stars ;
Or while the balmy glooming, crescent-lit,
Spread the light haze along the river-shores,
And in the hollows ; or as once we met
Unheedful, tho' beneath a whispering rain
Night slid down one long stream of sighing wind,
And in her bosom bore the baby, Sleep.

   But this whole hour your eyes have been intent
On that veil'd picture—veil'd, for what it holds
May not be dwelt on by the common day.
This prelude has prepared thee.   Raise thy soul ;
Make thine heart ready with thine eyes : the time
Is come to raise the veil.
                              Behold her there,
As I beheld her ere she knew my heart,
My first, last love ; the idol of my youth,
The darling of my manhood, and, alas !
Now the most blessed memory of mine age.

EDWARD GRAY.

SWEET Emma Moreland of yonder town
 Met me walking on yonder way,
" And have you lost your heart ? " she said ;
 " And are you married yet, Edward Gray ? "

Sweet Emma Moreland spoke to me :
 Bitterly weeping I turn'd away :
" Sweet Emma Moreland, love no more
 Can touch the heart of Edward Gray.

" Ellen Adair she loved me well,
 Against her father's and mother's will :
To-day I sat for an hour and wept,
 By Ellen's grave, on the windy hill.

" Shy she was, and I thought her cold ;
 Thought her proud, and fled over the sea ;
Fill'd I was with folly and spite,
 When Ellen Adair was dying for me.

" Cruel, cruel the words I said !
 Cruelly came they back to-day :
' You're too slight and fickle,' I said,
 ' To trouble the heart of Edward Gray.'

" There I put my face in the grass—
 Whisper'd, ' Listen to my despair :
I repent me of all I did :
 Speak a little, Ellen Adair ! '

" Then I took a pencil, and wrote
    On the mossy stone, as I lay,
' Here lies the body of Ellen Adair ;
    And here the heart of Edward Gray ! '

" Love may come, and love may go,
    And fly, like a bird, from tree to tree :
But I will love no more, no more,
    Till Ellen Adair come back to me.

" Bitterly wept I over the stone :
    Bitterly weeping I turn'd away :
There lies the body of Ellen Adair !
    And there the heart of Edward Gray ! "

LOVE AND DEATH.

WHAT time the mighty moon was gathering light
Love paced the thymy plots of Paradise,
And all about him roll'd his lustrous eyes ;
When, turning round a cassia, full in view
Death, walking all alone beneath a yew,
And talking to himself, first met his sight :
" You must begone," said Death, " these walks are
    mine."
Love wept and spread his sheeny vans for flight ;
Yet ere he parted said, " This hour is thine :
Thou art the shadow of life, and as the tree
Stands in the sun and shadows all beneath,
So in the light of great eternity
Life eminent creates the shade of death ;
The shadow passeth when the tree shall fall,
But I shall reign for ever over all."

THE DAY-DREAM.

PROLOGUE.

O, LADY FLORA, let me speak :
  A pleasant hour has past away
While, dreaming on your damask cheek,
  The dewy sister-eyelids lay.
As by the lattice you reclined,
  I went thro' many wayward moods
To see you dreaming—and, behind,
  A summer crisp with shining woods.
And I too dream'd, until at last
  Across my fancy, brooding warm,
The reflex of a legend past,
  And loosely settled into form.
And would you have the thought I had,
  And see the vision that I saw,
Then take the broidery-frame, and add
  A crimson to the quaint Macaw,
And I will tell it. Turn your face,
  Nor look with that too-earnest eye—
The rhymes are dazzled from their place,
  And order'd words asunder fly.

I.

THE SLEEPING PALACE.

THE varying year with blade and sheaf
  Clothes and reclothes the happy plains ;
Here rests the sap within the leaf,
  Here stays the blood along the veins.
Faint shadows, vapours lightly curl'd,
  Faint murmurs from the meadows come,

Like hints and echoes of the world
　　To spirits folded in the womb.

Soft lustre bathes the range of urns
　　On every slanting terrace-lawn.
The fountain to his place returns
　　Deep in the garden lake withdrawn.
Here droops the banner on the tower,
　　On the hall-hearths the festal fires,
The peacock in his laurel bower,
　　The parrot in his gilded wires.

Roof-haunting martins warm their eggs :
　　In these, in those the life is stay'd.
The mantles from the golden pegs
　　Droop sleepily : no sound is made,
Not even of a gnat that sings.
　　More like a picture seemeth all
Than those old portraits of old kings,
　　That watch the sleepers from the wall.

Here sits the Butler with a flask
　　Between his knees, half-drain'd ; and there
The wrinkled steward at his task,
　　The maid-of-honour blooming fair :
The page has caught her hand in his :
　　Her lips are sever'd as to speak :
His own are pouted to a kiss :
　　The blush is fix'd upon her cheek.

Till all the hundred summers pass,
　　The beams, that thro' the Oriel shine,
Make prisms in every carven glass,
　　And beaker brimm'd with noble wine,

Each baron at the banquet sleeps,
   Grave faces gather'd in a ring.
His state the king reposing keeps.
   He must have been a jovial king.

All round a hedge upshoots, and shows
   At distance like a little wood ;
Thorns, ivies, woodbine, misletoes,
   And grapes with bunches red as blood ;
All creeping plants, a wall of green
   Close-matted, bur and brake and briar,
And glimpsing over these, just seen,
   High up, the topmost palace-spire.

When will the hundred summers die,
   And thought and time be born again,
And newer knowledge, drawing nigh,
   Bring truth that sways the soul of men ?
Here all things in their place remain,
   As all were order'd, ages since.
Come, Care and Pleasure, Hope and Pain,
   And bring the fated fairy Prince.

II.

THE SLEEPING BEAUTY.

YEAR after year unto her feet,
   She lying on her couch alone,
Across the purpled coverlet,
   The maiden's jet-black hair has grown,
On either side her tranced form
   Forth streaming from a braid of pearl :
The slumbrous light is rich and warm,
   And moves not on the rounded curl.

The silk star-broider'd coverlid
  Unto her limbs itself doth mould
Languidly ever ; and, amid
  Her full black ringlets downward roll'd,
Glows forth each softly-shadow'd arm
  With bracelets of the diamond bright :
Her constant beauty doth inform
  Stillness with love, and day with light.

She sleeps : her breathings are not heard
  In palace chambers far apart.
The fragrant tresses are not stirr'd
  That lie upon her charmed heart.
She sleeps : on either hand upswells
  The gold-fringed pillow lightly prest :
She sleeps, nor dreams, but ever dwells
  A perfect form in perfect rest.

III.

THE ARRIVAL.

ALL precious things, discover'd late,
  To those that seek them issue forth ;
For love in sequel works with fate,
  And draws the veil from hidden worth.
He travels far from other skies—
  His mantle glitters on the rocks—
A fairy Prince, with joyful eyes,
  And lighter-footed than the fox.

The bodies and the bones of those
  That strove in other days to pass,
Are wither'd in the thorny close,
  Or scatter'd blanching on the grass,

He gazes on the silent dead :
　　" They perish'd in their daring deeds."
This proverb flashes thro' his head,
　　" The many fail : the one succeeds."

He comes, scarce knowing what he seeks :
　　He breaks the hedge : he enters there :
The colour flies into his cheeks :
　　He trusts to light on something fair ;
For all his life the charm did talk
　　About his path, and hover near
With words of promise in his walk,
　　And whisper'd voices at his ear.

More close and close his footsteps wind ;
　　The Magic Music in his heart
Beats quick and quicker, till he find
　　The quiet chamber far apart.
His spirit flutters like a lark,
　　He stoops—to kiss her—on his knee.
" Love, if thy tresses be so dark,
　　How dark those hidden eyes must be ! "

IV.
THE REVIVAL.

A TOUCH, a kiss ! the charm was snapt.
　　There rose a noise of striking clocks,
And feet that ran, and doors that clapt,
　　And barking dogs, and crowing cocks ;
A fuller light illumined all,
　　A breeze thro' all the garden swept,
A sudden hubbub shook the hall,
　　And sixty feet the fountain leapt.

The hedge broke in, the banner blew,
   The butler drank, the steward scrawl'd,
The fire shot up, the martin flew,
   The parrot scream'd, the peacock squall'd,
The maid and page renew'd their strife,
   The palace bang'd, and buzz'd and clackt,
And all the long-pent stream of life
   Dash'd downward in a cataract.

And last with these the king awoke,
   And in his chair himself uprear'd,
And yawn'd, and rubb'd his face, and spoke,
   " By holy rood, a royal beard !
How say you ? we have slept, my lords.
   My beard has grown into my lap."
The barons swore, with many words,
   'Twas but an after-dinner's nap.

" Pardy," return'd the king, " but still
   My joints are something stiff or so.
My lord, and shall we pass the bill
   I mention'd half an hour ago ? "
The chancellor, sedate and vain,
   In courteous words return'd reply :
But dallied with his golden chain,
   And, smiling, put the question by.

V.

THE DEPARTURE.

AND on her lover's arm she leant,
   And round her waist she felt it fold,
And far across the hills they went
   In that new world which is the old ;

Across the hills, and far away
  Beyond their utmost purple rim,
And deep into the dying day
  The happy princess follow'd him.

" I'd sleep another hundred years,
  O love, for such another kiss ; "
" O wake for ever, love," she hears,
  " O love, 'twas such as this and this."
And o'er them many a sliding star,
  And many a merry wind was borne,
And, stream'd thro' many a golden bar,
  The twilight melted into morn.

" O eyes long laid in happy sleep ! "
  " O happy sleep, that lightly fled ! "
" O happy kiss, that woke thy sleep ! "
  " O love, thy kiss would wake the dead ! "
And o'er them many a flowing range
  Of vapour buoy'd the crescent-bark,
And, rapt thro' many a rosy change,
  The twilight died into the dark.

" A hundred summers ! can it be ?
  And whither goest thou, tell me where ? "
" O seek my father's court with me,
  For there are greater wonders there."
And o'er the hills, and far away
  Beyond their utmost purple rim,
Beyond the night, across the day,
  Thro' all the world she follow'd him.

VI.

MORAL.

So, Lady Flora, take my lay,
   And if you find no moral there,
Go, look in any glass and say,
   What moral is in being fair.
Oh, to what uses shall we put
   The wildweed-flower that simply blows ?
And is there any moral shut
   Within the bosom of the rose ?

But any man that walks the mead,
   In bud or blade, or bloom, may find,
According as his humours lead,
   A meaning suited to his mind.
And liberal applications lie
   In Art like Nature, dearest friend ;
So 'twere to cramp its use, if I
   Should hook it to some useful end.

VII.

L'ENVOI.

You shake your head.   A random string
   Your finer female sense offends.
Well—were it not a pleasant thing
   To fall asleep with all one's friends ;
To pass with all our social ties
   To silence from the paths of men ;
And every hundred years to rise
   And learn the world, and sleep again ;

To sleep thro' terms of mighty wars,
    And wake on science grown to more,
On secrets of the brain, the stars,
    As wild as aught of fairy lore ;
And all that else the years will show,
    The Poet-forms of stronger hours,
The vast Republics that may grow,
    The Federations and the Powers ;
Titanic forces taking birth
    In divers seasons, divers climes ;
For we are Ancients of the earth,
    And in the morning of the times.

So sleeping, so aroused from sleep
    Thro' sunny decads new and strange,
Or gay quinquenniads would we reap
    The flower and quintessence of change.

Ah, yet would I—and would I might !
    So much your eyes my fancy take—
Be still the first to leap to light
    That I might kiss those eyes awake !
For, am I right or am I wrong,
    To choose your own you did not care ;
You'd have *my* moral from the song,
    And I will take my pleasure there :
And, am I right or am I wrong,
    My fancy, ranging thro' and thro',
To search a meaning for the song,
    Perforce will still revert to you ;
Nor finds a closer truth than this
    All-graceful head, so richly curl'd,

And evermore a costly kiss
   The prelude to some brighter world.
For since the time when Adam first
   Embraced his Eve in happy hour,
And every bird of Eden burst
   In carol, every bud to flower,
What eyes, like thine, have waken'd hopes?
   What lips, like thine, so sweetly join'd?
Where on the double rosebud droops
   The fullness of the pensive mind ;
Which all too dearly self-involved,
   Yet sleeps a dreamless sleep to me ;
A sleep by kisses undissolved,
   That lets thee neither hear nor see :
But break it.   In the name of wife,
   And in the rights that name may give,
Are clasp'd the moral of thy life,
   And that for which I care to live.

EPILOGUE.

So, Lady Flora, take my lay,
   And, if you find a meaning there,
O whisper to your glass, and say,
   " What wonder, if he thinks me fair? "
What wonder I was all unwise,
   To shape the song for your delight
Like long-tail'd birds of Paradise,
   That float thro' Heaven, and cannot light?
Or old-world trains, upheld at court
   By Cupid-boys of blooming hue—
But take it—earnest wed with sport,
   And either sacred unto you.

THE MILLER'S DAUGHTER.

I SEE the wealthy miller yet,
    His double chin, his portly size,
And who that knew him could forget
    The busy wrinkles round his eyes?
The slow wise smile that, round about
    His dusty forehead drily curl'd,
Seem'd half-within and half-without,
    And full of dealings with the world?

In yonder chair I see him sit,
    Three fingers round the old silver cup—
I see his gray eyes twinkle yet
    At his own jest—gray eyes lit up
With summer lightnings of a soul
    So full of summer warmth, so glad,
So healthy, sound, and clear and whole,
    His memory scarce can make me sad.

Yet fill my glass : give me one kiss :
    My own sweet Alice, we must die.
There's somewhat in this world amiss
    Shall be unriddled by and by.
There's somewhat flows to us in life,
    But more is taken quite away.
Pray, Alice, pray, my darling wife,
    That we may die the self-same day.

Have I not found a happy earth ?
  I least should breathe a thought of pain.
Would God renew me from my birth
  I'd almost live my life again.
So sweet it seems with thee to walk,
  And once again to woo thee mine—
It seems in after-dinner talk
  Across the walnuts and the wine—

To be the long and listless boy
  Late-left an orphan of the squire,
Where this old mansion mounted high
  Looks down upon the village spire :
For even here, where I and you
  Have lived and loved alone so long,
Each morn my sleep was broken thro'
  By some wild skylark's matin song.

And oft I heard the tender dove
  In firry woodlands making moan ;
But ere I saw your eyes, my love,
  I had no motion of my own.
For scarce my life with fancy play'd
  Before I dream'd that pleasant dream—
Still hither thither idly sway'd
  Like those long mosses in the stream.

Or from the bridge I lean'd to hear
  The milldam rushing down with noise,
And see the minnows everywhere
  In crystal eddies glance and poise,

6

The tall flag-flowers when they sprung
  Below the range of stepping-stones,
Or those three chestnuts near, that hung
  In masses thick with milky cones.

But, Alice, what an hour was that,
  When after roving in the woods
('Twas April then), I came and sat
  Below the chestnuts, when their buds
Were glistening to the breezy blue ;
  And on the slope, an absent fool,
I cast me down, nor thought of you,
  But angled in the higher pool.

A love-song I had somewhere read,
  An echo from a measured strain,
Beat time to nothing in my head
  From some odd corner of the brain.
It haunted me, the morning long,
  With weary sameness in the rhymes,
The phantom of a silent song,
  That went and came a thousand times.

Then leapt a trout.   In lazy mood
  I watch'd the little circles die ;
They past into the level flood,
  And there a vision caught my eye ;
The reflex of a beauteous form,
  A glowing arm, a gleaming neck,
As when a sunbeam wavers warm
  Within the dark and dimpled beck.

For you remember, you had set,
   That morning, on the casement's edge
A long green box of mignonette,
   And you were leaning from the ledge:
And when I raised my eyes, above
   They met with two so full and bright—
Such eyes!   I swear to you, my love,
   That these have never lost their light.

I loved, and love dispell'd the fear
   That I should die an early death :
For love possess'd the atmosphere,
   And fill'd the breast with purer breath.
My mother thought, What ails the boy?
   For I was alter'd, and began
To move about the house with joy,
   And with the certain step of man.

I loved the brimming wave that swam
   Thro' quiet meadows round the mill,
The sleepy pool above the dam,
   The pool beneath it never still,
The meal-sacks on the whiten'd floor,
   The dark round of the dripping wheel,
The very air about the door
   Made misty with the floating meal.

And oft in ramblings on the wold,
   When April nights began to blow,
And April's crescent glimmer'd cold,
   I saw the village light below ;

I knew your taper far away,
   And full at heart of trembling hope,
From off the wold I came, and lay
   Upon the freshly-flower'd slope.

The deep brook groan'd beneath the mill ;
   And " by that lamp," I thought, " she sits ! "
The white chalk-quarry from the hill
   Gleam'd to the flying moon by fits.
" O that I were beside her now !
   O will she answer if I call ?
O would she give me vow for vow,
   Sweet Alice, if I told her all ? "

Sometimes I saw you sit and spin ;
   And, in the pauses of the wind,
Sometimes I heard you sing within ;
   Sometimes your shadow cross'd the blind.
At last you rose and moved the light,
   And the long shadow of the chair
Flitted across into the night,
   And all the casement darken'd there.

But when at last I dared to speak,
   The lanes, you know, were white with may,
Your ripe lips moved not, but your cheek
   Flush'd like the coming of the day ;
And so it was—half-sly, half-shy,
   You would, and would not, little one !
Although I pleaded tenderly,
   And you and I were all alone.

And slowly was my mother brought
   To yield consent to my desire ;
She wish'd me happy, but she thought
   I might have look'd a little higher ;
And I was young—too young to wed :
   " Yet must I love her for your sake ;
Go fetch your Alice here," she said :
   Her eyelid quiver'd as she spake.

And down I went to fetch my bride :
   But, Alice, you were ill at ease ;
This dress and that by turns you tried,
   Too fearful that you should not please.
I loved you better for your fears,
   I knew you could not look but well ;
And dews, that would have fall'n in tears,
   I kissed away before they fell.

I watch'd the little flutterings,
   The doubt my mother would not see ;
She spoke at large of many things,
   And at the last she spoke of me ;
And turning look'd upon your face,
   As near this door you sat apart,
And rose, and, with a silent grace
   Approaching, press'd you heart to heart.

Ah, well—but sing the foolish song
   I gave you, Alice, on the day
When, arm in arm, we went along,
   A pensive pair, and you were gay

With bridal flowers—that I may seem,
   As in the nights of old, to lie
Beside the mill-wheel in the stream,
   While those full chestnuts whisper by.

     It is the miller's daughter,
       And she is grown so dear, so dear,
     That I would be the jewel
       That trembles at her ear :
     For hid in ringlets day and night,
     I'd touch her neck so warm and white.

     And I would be the girdle
       About her dainty dainty waist,
     And her heart would beat against me,
       In sorrow and in rest :
     And I should know if it beat right,
     I'd clasp it round so close and tight.

     And I would be the necklace,
       And all day long to fall and rise
     Upon her balmy bosom,
       With her laughter or her sighs,
     And I would lie so light, so light,
     I scarce should be unclasp'd at night.

A trifle, sweet ! which true love spells—
   True love interprets—right alone.
His light upon the letter dwells,
   For all the spirit is his own.
So, if I waste words now, in truth
   You must blame Love.   His early rage
Had force to make me rhyme in youth,
   And makes me talk too much in age.

And now those vivid hours are gone,
   Like mine own life to me thou art,
Where Past and Present, wound in one,
   Do make a garland for the heart :

So sing that other song I made,
 Half-anger'd with my happy lot,
The day, when in the chestnut shade
 I found the blue Forget-me-not.

   Love that hath us in the net,
   Can he pass, and we forget?
   Many suns arise and set.
   Many a chance the years beget.
   Love the gift is Love the debt.
     Even so.
   Love is hurt with jar and fret.
   Love is made a vague regret.
   Eyes with idle tears are wet.
   Idle habit links us yet.
   What is love? for we forget:
     Ah, no! no!

Look thro' mine eyes with thine. True wife,
 Round my true heart thine arms entwine;
My other dearer life in life,
 Look thro' my very soul with thine!
Untouch'd with any shade of years,
 May those kind eyes for ever dwell!
They have not shed a many tears,
 Dear eyes, since first I knew them well.

Yet tears they shed: they had their part
 Of sorrow: for when time was ripe,
The still affection of the heart
 Became an outward breathing type,
That into stillness past again,
 And left a want unknown before;
Although the loss that brought us pain,
 That loss but made us love the more,

With farther lookings on.   The kiss,
   The woven arms, seem but to be
Weak symbols of the settled bliss,
   The comfort, I have found in thee :
But that God bless thee, dear—who wrought
   Two spirits to one equal mind—
With blessings beyond hope or thought,
   With blessings which no words can find.

Arise, and let us wander forth,
   To yon old mill across the wolds ;
For look, the sunset, south and north,
   Winds all the vale in rosy folds,
And fires your narrow casement glass,
   Touching the sullen pool below :
On the chalk-hill the bearded grass
   Is dry and dewless.   Let us go.

LADY CLARA VERE DE VERE.

Lady Clara Vere de Vere,
   Of me you shall not win renown :
You thought to break a country heart
   For pastime, ere you went to town.
At me you smiled, but unbeguiled
   I saw the snare, and I retired :
The daughter of a hundred Earls,
   You are not one to be desired.

Lady Clara Vere de Vere,
   I know you proud to bear your name,
Your pride is yet no mate for mine,
   Too proud to care from whence I came.

Nor would I break for your sweet sake
  A heart that doats on truer charms.
A simple maiden in her flower
  Is worth a hundred coats-of-arms.

Lady Clara Vere de Vere,
  Some meeker pupil you must find,
For were you queen of all that is,
  I could not stoop to such a mind.
You sought to prove how I could love,
  And my disdain is my reply.
The lion on your old stone gates
  Is not more cold to you than I.

Lady Clara Vere de Vere,
  You put strange memories in my head.
Not thrice your branching limes have blown
  Since I beheld young Laurence dead.
Oh your sweet eyes, your low replies :
  A great enchantress you may be ;
But there was that across his throat
  Which you had hardly cared to see.

Lady Clara Vere de Vere,
  When thus he met his mother's view,
She had the passions of her kind,
  She spake some certain truths of you.
Indeed I heard one bitter word
  That scarce is fit for you to hear ;
Her manners had not that repose
  Which stamps the caste of Vere de Vere.

Lady Clara Vere de Vere,
    There stands a spectre in your hall :
The guilt of blood is at your door :
    You changed a wholesome heart to gall.
You held your course without remorse,
    To make him trust his modest worth,
And, last, you fix'd a vacant stare,
    And slew him with your noble birth.

Trust me, Clara Vere de Vere,
    From yon blue heavens above us bent
The grand old gardener and his wife
    Smile at the claims of long descent.
Howe'er it be, it seems to me,
    'Tis only noble to be good.
Kind hearts are more than coronets,
    And simple faith than Norman blood.

I know you, Clara Vere de Vere :
    You pine among your halls and towers :
The languid light of your proud eyes
    Is wearied of the rolling hours.
In glowing health, with boundless wealth,
    But sickening of a vague disease,
You know so ill to deal with time,
    You needs must play such pranks as these.

Clara, Clara Vere de Vere,
    If time be heavy on your hands,
Are there no beggars at your gate,
    Nor any poor about your lands ?

Oh ! teach the orphan-boy to read,
  Or teach the orphan-girl to sew,
Pray Heaven for a human heart,
  And let the foolish yeoman go.

THE SISTERS.

WE were two daughters of one race :
She was the fairest in the face :
  The wind is blowing in turret and tree.
They were together, and she fell ;
Therefore revenge became me well.
  O the Earl was fair to see !

She died : she went to burning flame :
She mix'd her ancient blood with shame.
  The wind is howling in turret and tree.
Whole weeks and months, and early and late,
To win his love I lay in wait :
  O the Earl was fair to see !

I made a feast ; I bad him come ;
I won his love, I brought him home.
  The wind is roaring in turret and tree.
And after supper, on a bed,
Upon my lap he laid his head :
  O the Earl was fair to see !

I kiss'd his eyelids into rest :
His ruddy cheek upon my breast.
  The wind is raging in turret and tree.
I hated him with the hate of hell,
But I loved his beauty passing well.
  O the Earl was fair to see !

I rose up in the silent night :
I made my dagger sharp and bright.
   The wind is raving in turret and tree.
As half-asleep his breath he drew,
Three time I stabb'd him thro' and thro'.
   O the Earl was fair to see !

I curl'd and comb'd his comely head,
He look'd so grand when he was dead.
   The wind is blowing in turret and tree.
I wrapt his body in the sheet,
And laid him at his mother's feet.
   O the Earl was fair to see !

LOCKSLEY HALL.

COMRADES, leave me here a little, while as yet 'tis
   early morn :
Leave me here, and when you want me, sound upon
   the bugle horn.

'Tis the place, and all around it, as of old, the
   curlews call,
Dreary gleams about the moorland flying over
   Locksley Hall ;

Locksley Hall, that in the distance overlooks the
   sandy tracts,
And the hollow ocean-ridges roaring into cata-
racts.

Many a night from yonder ivied casement, ere I
    went to rest,
Did I look on great Orion sloping slowly to the
    West.

Many a night I saw the Pleiads, rising thro' the
    mellow shade,
Glitter like a swarm of fire-flies tangled in a silver
    braid.

Here about the beach I wander'd, nourishing a
    youth sublime
With the fairy tales of science, and the long result
    of Time ;

When the centuries behind me like a fruitful land
    reposed ;
When I clung to all the present for the promise
    that it closed :

When I dipt into the future far as human eye could
    see ;
Saw the Vision of the world, and all the wonder
    that would be.——

In the Spring a fuller crimson comes upon the robin's
    breast ;
In the Spring the wanton lapwing gets himself
    another crest ;

In the Spring a livelier iris changes on the burnish'd
    dove ;
In the Spring a young man's fancy lightly turns to
    thoughts of love.

Then her cheek was pale and thinner than should
    be for one so young,
And her eyes on all my motions with a mute
    observance hung.

And I said, " My cousin Amy, speak, and speak the
    truth to me,
Trust me, cousin, all the current of my being sets
    to thee."

On her pallid cheek and forehead came a colour and
    a light,
As I have seen the rosy red flushing in the northern
    night.

And she turn'd—her bosom shaken with a sudden
    storm of sighs—
All the spirit deeply dawning in the dark of hazel
    eyes—

Saying, " I have hid my feelings, fearing they should
    do me wrong ; "
Saying, " Dost thou love me, cousin ? " weeping,
    " I have loved thee long."

Love took up the glass of Time, and turn'd it in
    his glowing hands ;
Every moment, lightly shaken, ran itself in golden
    sands.

Love took up the harp of Life, and smote on all the
    chords with might ;
Smote the chord of Self, that, trembling, pass'd in
    music out of sight.

Many a morning on the moorland did we hear the
  copses ring,
And her whisper throng'd my pulses with the fullness
  of the Spring.

Many an evening by the waters did we watch the
  stately ships,
And our spirits rush'd together at the touching of
  the lips.

O my cousin, shallow-hearted ! O my Amy, mine
  no more !
O the dreary, dreary moorland ! O the barren,
  barren shore !

Falser than all fancy fathoms, falser than all songs
  have sung,
Puppet to a father's threat, and servile to a shrewish
  tongue !

Is it well to wish thee happy ?—having known me—
  to decline
On a range of lower feelings and a narrower heart
  than mine !

Yet it shall be : thou shalt lower to his level day
  by day,
What is fine within thee growing coarse to sym-
  pathise with clay.

As the husband is, the wife is : thou art mated with
  a clown,
And the grossness of his nature will have weight to
  drag thee down.

He will hold thee, when his passion shall have spent
    its novel force,
Something better than his dog, a little dearer than
    his horse.

What is this? his eyes are heavy : think not they
    are glazed with wine.
Go to him : it is thy duty : kiss him : take his hand
    in thine.

It may be my lord is weary, that his brain is over-
    wrought :
Soothe him with thy finer fancies, touch him with
    thy lighter thought.

He will answer to the purpose, easy things to under-
    stand—
Better thou wert dead before me, tho' I slew thee
    with my hand !

Better thou and I were lying, hidden from the heart's
    disgrace,
Roll'd in one another's arms, and silent in a last
    embrace.

Cursed be the social wants that sin against the
    strength of youth !
Cursed be the social lies that warp us from the living
    truth !

Cursed be the sickly forms that err from honest
    Nature's rule !
Cursed be the gold that gilds the straiten'd forehead
    of the fool !

Well—'tis well that I should bluster !—Hadst thou
    less unworthy proved—
Would to God—for I had loved thee more than ever
    wife was loved.

Am I mad, that I should cherish that which bears but
    bitter fruit ?
I will pluck it from my bosom, tho' my heart be at
    the root.

Never, tho' my mortal summers to such length of
    years should come
As the many-winter'd crow that leads the clanging
    rookery home.

Where is comfort? in division of the records of the
    mind ?
Can I part her from herself, and love her, as I knew
    her, kind ?

I remember one that perish'd : sweetly did she speak
    and move :
Such a one do I remember, whom to look at was to
    love.

Can I think of her as dead, and love her for the love
    she bore ?
No—she never loved me truly : love is love for ever-
    more.

Comfort ? comfort scorn'd of devils ! this is truth
    the poet sings,
That a sorrow's crown of sorrow is remembering
    happier things.

Drug thy memories, lest thou learn it, lest thy heart
    be put to proof,
In the dead unhappy night, and when the rain is on
    the roof.

Like a dog, he hunts in dreams, and thou art staring
    at the wall,
Where the dying night-lamp flickers, and the shadows
    rise and fall.

Then a hand shall pass before thee, pointing to his
    drunken sleep,
To thy widow'd marriage-pillows, to the tears that
    thou wilt weep.

Thou shalt hear the " Never, never," whisper'd by
    the phantom years,
And a song from out the distance in the ringing of
    thine ears ;

And an eye shall vex thee, looking ancient kindness
    on thy pain.
Turn thee, turn thee on thy pillow : get thee to thy
    rest again.

Nay, but Nature brings thee solace ; for a tender
    voice will cry.
'Tis a purer life than thine ; a lip to drain thy trouble
    dry.

Baby lips will laugh me down : my latest rival brings
    thee rest.
Baby fingers, waxen touches, press me from the
    mother's breast.

O, the child too clothes the father with a dearness
    not his due.
Half is thine and half is his : it will be worthy of
    the two.

O, I see thee old and formal, fitted to thy petty
    part,
With a little hoard of maxims preaching down a
    daughter's heart.

" They were dangerous guides the feelings—she
    herself was not exempt—
Truly, she herself had suffer'd "—Perish in thy self-
    contempt !

Overlive it—lower yet—be happy ! wherefore should
    I care ?
I myself must mix with action, lest I wither by
    despair.

What is that which I should turn to, lighting upon
    days like these ?
Every door is barr'd with gold, and opens but to
    golden keys.

Every gate is throng'd with suitors, all the markets
    overflow.
I have but an angry fancy : what is that which I
    should do ?

I had been content to perish, falling on the foeman's
    ground,
When the ranks are roll'd in vapour, and the winds
    are laid with sound.

But the jingling of the guinea helps the hurt that
    Honour feels,
And the nations do but murmur, snarling at each
    other's heels.

Can I but relive in sadness ?   I will turn that earlier
    page.
Hide me from my deep emotion, O thou wondrous
    Mother-Age !

Make me feel the wild pulsation that I felt before
    the strife,
When I heard my days before me, and the tumult of
    my life ;

Yearning for the large excitement that the coming
    years would yield,
Eager-hearted as a boy when first he leaves his
    father's field,

And at night along the dusky highway near and
    nearer drawn,
Sees in heaven the light of London flaring like a
    dreary dawn ;

And his spirit leaps within him to be gone before
    him then,
Underneath the light he looks at, in among the
    throngs of men ;

Men, my brothers, men the workers, ever reaping
    something new :
That which they have done but earnest of the things
    that they shall do :

For I dipt into the future, far as human eye could
see,
Saw the Vision of the world, and all the wonder that
would be ;

Saw the heavens fill with commerce, argosies of
magic sails,
Pilots of the purple twilight, dropping down with
costly bales ;

Heard the heavens fill with shouting, and there
rain'd a ghastly dew
From the nations' airy navies grappling in the central
blue ;

Far along the world-wide whisper of the south-wind
rushing warm,
With the standards of the peoples plunging thro' the
thunder-storm ;

Till the war-drum throbb'd no longer, and the battle-
flags were furl'd
In the Parliament of man, the Federation of the
world.

There the common sense of most shall hold a fretful
realm in awe,
And the kindly earth shall slumber, lapt in universal
law.

So I triumph'd, ere my passion sweeping thro' me
left me dry,
Left me with the palsied heart, and left me with the
jaundiced eye ;

Eye, to which all order festers, all things here are
    out of joint,
Science moves, but slowly slowly, creeping on from
    point to point :

Slowly comes a hungry people, as a lion, creeping
    nigher,
Glares at one that nods and winks behind a slowly-
    dying fire.

Yet I doubt not thro' the ages one increasing
    purpose runs,
And the thoughts of men are widen'd with the
    process of the suns.

What is that to him that reaps not harvest of his
    youthful joys,
Tho' the deep heart of existence beat for ever like
    a boy's ?

Knowledge comes, but wisdom lingers, and I linger
    on the shore,
And the individual withers, and the world is more
    and more.

Knowledge comes, but wisdom lingers, and he bears
    a laden breast,
Full of sad experience, moving toward the stillness
    of his rest.

Hark, my merry comrades call me, sounding on the
    bugle-horn,
They to whom my foolish passion were a target for
    their scorn :

Shall it not be scorn to me to harp on such a
    moulder'd string ?
I am shamed thro' all my nature to have loved so
    slight a thing.

Weakness to be wroth with weakness ! woman's
    pleasure, woman's pain—
Nature made them blinder motions bounded in a
    shallower brain :

Woman is the lesser man, and all thy passions,
    match'd with mine,
Are as moonlight unto sunlight, and as water unto
    wine—

Here at least, where nature sickens, nothing. Ah,
    for some retreat
Deep in yonder shining Orient, where my life began
    to beat ;

Where in wild Mahratta-battle fell my father evil-
    starr'd ;—
I was left a trampled orphan, and a selfish uncle's
    ward.

Or to burst all links of habit—there to wander far
    away,
On from island unto island at the gateways of the
    day.

Larger constellations burning, mellow moons and
    happy skies,
Breadths of tropic shade and palms in cluster, knots
    of Paradise.

Never comes the trader, never floats an European
flag,
Slides the bird o'er lustrous woodland, swings the
trailer from the crag ;—

Droops the heavy-blossom'd bower, hangs the heavy-
fruited tree—
Summer isles of Eden lying in dark-purple spheres
of sea.

There methinks would be enjoyment more than in
this march of mind,
In the steamship, in the railway, in the thoughts that
shake mankind.

There the passions cramp'd no longer shall have
scope and breathing-space ;
I will take some savage woman, she shall rear my
dusky race.

Iron-jointed, supple-sinew'd, they shall dive, and
they shall run,
Catch the wild goat by the hair, and hurl their lances
in the sun ;

Whistle back the parrot's call, and leap the rainbows
of the brooks,
Not with blinded eyesight poring over miserable
books—

Fool, again the dream, the fancy ! but I *know* my
words are wild,
But I count the gray barbarian lower than the
Christian child,

I, to herd with narrow foreheads, vacant of our
    glorious gains,
Like a beast with lower pleasures, like a beast with
    lower pains !

Mated with a squalid savage—what to me were sun
    or clime ?
I the heir of all the ages, in the foremost files of
    time—

I that rather held it better men should perish one
    by one,
Than that earth should stand at gaze like Joshua's
    moon in Ajalon !

Not in vain the distance beacons. Forward, forward
    let us range.
Let the great world spin for ever down the ringing
    grooves of change.

Thro' the shadow of the globe we sweep into the
    younger day :
Better fifty years of Europe than a cycle of
    Cathay.

Mother-Age (for mine I knew not) help me as when
    life begun :
Rift the hills, and roll the waters, flash the light-
    nings, weigh the Sun—

O, I see the crescent promise of my spirit hath
    not set.
Ancient founts of inspiration well thro' all my
    fancy yet.

Howsoever these things be, a long farewell to
  Locksley Hall!
Now for me the woods may wither, now for me the
  roof-tree fall.

Comes a vapour from the margin, blackening over
  heath and holt,
Cramming all the blast before it, in its breast a
  thunderbolt.

Let it fall on Locksley Hall, with rain or hail, or
  fire or snow ;
For the mighty wind arises, roaring seaward, and I go.

BREAK, BREAK, BREAK.

BREAK, break, break,
  On thy cold gray stones, O Sea !
And I would that my tongue could utter
  The thoughts that arise in me.

O well for the fisherman's boy,
  That he shouts with his sister at play !
O well for the sailor lad,
  That he sings in his boat on the bay !

And the stately ships go on
  To their haven under the hill ;
But O for the touch of a vanish'd hand,
  And the sound of a voice that is still !

Break, break, break,
  At the foot of thy crags, O Sea !
But the tender grace of a day that is dead
  Will never come back to me.

THE POET.

THE poet in a golden clime was born,
    With golden stars above ;
Dower'd with the hate of hate, the scorn of scorn,
    The love of love.

He saw thro' life and death, thro' good and ill,
    He saw thro' his own soul.
The marvel of the everlasting will,
    An open scroll,

Before him lay : with echoing feet he threaded
    The secretest walks of fame :
The viewless arrows of his thoughts were headed
    And wing'd with flame,

Like Indian reeds blown from his silver tongue,
    And of so fierce a flight,
From Calpe unto Caucasus they sung,
    Filling with light

And vagrant melodies the wind which bore
    Them earthward till they lit ;
Then, like the arrow-seeds of the field flower,
    The fruitful wit

Cleaving, took root, and springing forth anew
    Where'er they fell, behold,
Like to the mother plant in semblance, grew
    A flower all gold,

And bravely furnish'd all abroad to fling
    The winged shafts of truth,
To throng with stately blooms the breathing spring
    Of Hope and Youth.

So many minds did gird their orbs with beams,
    Tho' one did fling the fire.
Heaven flow'd upon the soul in many dreams
    Of high desire.

Thus truth was multiplied on truth, the world
    Like one great garden show'd,
And thro' the wreaths of floating dark upcurl'd,
    Rare sunrise flow'd.

And Freedom rear'd in that august sunrise
    Her beautiful bold brow,
When rites and forms before his burning eyes
    Melted like snow.

There was no blood upon her maiden robes
    Sunn'd by those orient skies ;
But round about the circles of the globes
    Of her keen eyes

And in her raiment's hem was traced in flame
    Wisdom, a name to shake
All evil dreams of power—a sacred name.
    And when she spake,

Her words did gather thunder as they ran,
    And as the lightning to the thunder
Which follows it, riving the spirit of man,
    Making earth wonder,

So was their meaning to her words.   No sword
    Of wrath her right arm whirl'd,
But one poor poet's scroll, and with *his* word
    She shook the world.

LOVE THOU THY LAND.

Love thou thy land, with love far-brought
    From out the storied Past, and used
    Within the Present, but transfused
Thro' future time by power of thought.

True love turn'd round on fixed poles,
    Love, that endures not sordid ends,
    For English natures, freemen, friends,
Thy brothers and immortal souls.

But pamper not a hasty time,
    Nor feed with crude imaginings
    The herd, wild hearts and feeble wings,
That every sophister can lime.

Deliver not the tasks of might
    To weakness, neither hide the ray
    From those, not blind, who wait for day,
Tho' sitting girt with doubtful light.

Make knowledge circle with the winds ;
    But let her herald, Reverence, fly
    Before her to whatever sky
Bear seed of men and growth of minds.

Watch what main-currents draw the years :
　　Cut Prejudice against the grain :
　　But gentle words are always gain :
Regard the weakness of thy peers :

Nor toil for title, place, or touch
　　Of pension, neither count on praise :
　　It grows to guerdon after-days :
Nor deal in watch-words over-much ;

Not clinging to some ancient saw ;
　　Not master'd by some modern term ;
　　Not swift nor slow to change, but firm :
And in its season bring the law ;

That from Discussion's lip may fall
　　With Life, that, working strongly, binds—
　　Set in all lights by many minds,
To close the interests of all.

For Nature also, cold and warm,
　　And moist and dry, devising long,
　　Thro' many agents making strong,
Matures the individual form.

Meet is it changes should control
　　Our being, lest we rust in ease.
　　We all are changed by still degrees,
All but the basis of the soul.

So let the change which comes be free
　　To ingroove itself with that, which flies,
　　And work, a joint of state, that plies
Its office, moved with sympathy.

A saying, hard to shape in act ;
   For all the past of Time reveals
   A bridal dawn of thunder-peals,
Wherever Thought hath wedded Fact.

Ev'n now we hear with inward strife
   A motion toiling in the gloom—-
   The Spirit of the years to come
Yearning to mix himself with Life.

A slow-develop'd strength awaits
   Completion in a painful school ;
   Phantoms of other forms of rule,
New Majesties of mighty States—

The warders of the growing hour,
   But vague in vapour, hard to mark ;
   And round them sea and air are dark
With great contrivances of Power.

Of many changes, aptly join'd,
   Is bodied forth the second whole.
   Regard gradation, lest the soul
Of Discord race the rising wind ;

A wind to puff your idol-fires,
   And heap their ashes on the head ;
   To shame the boast so often made,
That we are wiser than our sires.

Oh yet, if Nature's evil star
   Drive men in manhood, as in youth,
   To follow flying steps of Truth
Across the brazen bridge of war—

If New and Old, disastrous feud,
  Must ever shock, like armed foes,
  And this be true, till Time shall close,
That Principles are rain'd in blood ;

Not yet the wise of heart would cease
  To hold his hope thro' shame and guilt,
  But with his hand against the hilt,
Would pace the troubled land, like Peace ;

Not less, tho' dogs of Faction bay,
  Would serve his kind in deed and word,
  Certain, if knowledge bring the sword,
That knowledge takes the sword away—

Would love the gleams of good that broke
  From either side, nor veil his eyes :
  And if some dreadful need should rise
Would strike, and firmly, and one stroke :

To-morrow yet would reap to-day,
  As we bear blossom of the dead ;
  Earn well the thrifty months, nor wed
Raw Haste, half-sister to Delay.

THE EAGLE.

FRAGMENT.

HE clasps the crag with hooked hands ;
Close to the sun in lonely lands,
Ring'd with the azure world, he stands.

The wrinkled sea beneath him crawls ;
He watches from his mountain walls,
And like a thunderbolt he falls.

CLARIBEL.

A MELODY.

WHERE Claribel low-lieth
  The breezes pause and die,
    Letting the rose-leaves fall :
But the solemn oak-tree sigheth,
    Thick-leaved, ambrosial,
  With an ancient melody
  Of an inward agony,
Where Claribel low-lieth.

At eve the beetle boometh
  Athwart the thicket lone :
At noon the wild bee hummeth
  About the moss'd headstone :
At midnight the moon cometh,
  And looketh down alone.

Her song the lintwhite swelleth,
The clear-voiced mavis dwelleth,
  The callow throstle lispeth,
The slumbrous wave outwelleth,
  The babbling runnel crispeth,
The hollow grot replieth
Where Claribel low-lieth.

ADELINE.

MYSTERY of mysteries,
  Faintly smiling Adeline,
  Scarce of earth nor all divine,

8

Nor unhappy, nor at rest,
    But beyond expression fair
        With thy floating flaxen hair ;
Thy rose-lips and full blue eyes
    Take the heart from out my breast.
Wherefore those dim looks of thine,
Shadowy, dreaming Adeline ?

Whence that aery bloom of thine,
    Like a lily which the sun
Looks thro' in his sad decline,
    And a rose-bush leans upon,
Thou that faintly smilest still,
    As a Naiad in a well,
    Looking at the set of day,
Or a phantom two hours old
    Of a maiden past away,
Ere the placid lips be cold ?
Wherefore those faint smiles of thine,
    Spiritual Adeline ?

What hope or fear or joy is thine ?
Who talketh with thee, Adeline ?
    For sure thou art not all alone :
        Do beating hearts of salient springs
        Keep measure with thine own ?
            Hast thou heard the butterflies
            What they say betwixt their wings ?
            Or in stillest evenings
With what voice the violet woos
To his heart the silver dews ?
        Or when little airs arise,

How the merry bluebell rings
  To the mosses underneath ?
  Hast thou look'd upon the breath
Of the lilies at sunrise ?
Wherefore that faint smile of thine,
Shadowy, dreaming Adeline ?

Some honey-converse feeds thy mind,
  Some spirit of a crimson rose
  In love with thee forgets to close
  His curtains, wasting odorous sighs
All night long on darkness blind.
What aileth thee ? whom waitest thou
With thy soften'd, shadow'd brow,
  And those dew-lit eyes of thine,
  Thou faint smiler, Adeline ?

Lovest thou the doleful wind
  When thou gazest at the skies ?
Doth the low-tongued Orient
  Wander from the side of the morn,
  Dripping with Sabæan spice
On thy pillow, lowly bent
  With melodious airs lovelorn,
Breathing Light against thy face,
While his locks a-dropping twined
  Round thy neck in subtle ring
Make a carcanet of rays,
  And ye talk together still,
  In the language wherewith Spring
  Letters cowslips on the hill ?
Hence that look and smile of thine,
  Spiritual Adeline.

MARGARET.

O SWEET pale Margaret,
    O rare pale Margaret,
What lit your eyes with tearful power,
Like moonlight on a falling shower?
Who lent you, love, your mortal dower
    Of pensive thought and aspect pale,
    Your melancholy sweet and frail
As perfume of the cuckoo-flower?
From the westward-winding flood,
From the evening-lighted wood,
    From all things outward you have won
A tearful grace, as tho' you stood
    Between the rainbow and the sun.
The very smile before you speak,
That dimples your transparent cheek,
  Encircles all the heart, and feedeth
The senses with a still delight
    Of dainty sorrow without sound,
    Like the tender amber round,
  Which the moon about her spreadeth,
Moving thro' a fleecy night.

You love, remaining peacefully,
    To hear the murmur of the strife,
    But enter not the toil of life.
Your spirit is the calmed sea,
    Laid by the tumult of the fight.
You are the evening star, alway
    Remaining betwixt dark and bright :
Lull'd echoes of laborious day
    Come to you, gleams of mellow light
    Float by you on the verge of night.

What can it matter, Margaret,
    What songs below the waning stars
The lion-heart Plantagenet,
    Sang looking thro' his prison bars?
      Exquisite Margaret, who can tell
The last wild thought of Chatelet,
    Just ere the falling axe did part
      The burning brain from the true heart
        Even in her sight he loved so well?

A fairy shield your Genius made
    And gave you on your natal day.
Your sorrow, only sorrow's shade,
    Keeps real sorrow far away.
You move not in such solitudes,
    You are not less divine,
But more human in your moods,
    Than your twin-sister, Adeline.
Your hair is darker, and your eyes
    Touch'd with a somewhat darker hue,
    And less aërially blue,
    But ever trembling thro' the dew
Of dainty-woeful sympathies.

    O sweet pale Margaret,
    O rare pale Margaret,
Come down, come down, and hear me speak:
Tie up the ringlets on your cheek:
    The sun is just about to set,
The arching limes are tall and shady,
    And faint, rainy lights are seen,
      Moving in the leavy beech.

Rise from the feast of sorrow, lady,
   Where all day long you sit between
      Joy and woe, and whisper each.
Or only look across the lawn,
   Look out below your bower-eaves,
Look down, and let your blue eyes dawn
   Upon me thro' the jasmine-leaves.

MADELINE.

THOU art not steep'd in golden languors,
   No tranced summer calm is thine,
      Ever varying Madeline.
   Thro' light and shadow thou dost range,
   Sudden glances, sweet and strange,
Delicious spites and darling angers,
   And airy forms of flitting change.

Smiling, frowning, evermore,
Thou art perfect in love-lore.
Revealings deep and clear are thine
Of wealthy smiles : but who may know
Whether smile or frown be fleeter ?
Whether smile or frown be sweeter,
   Who may know ?
Frowns perfect-sweet along the brow
Light-glooming over eyes divine,
Like little clouds sun-fringed, are thine,
      Ever varying Madeline.
   Thy smile and frown are not aloof
    From one another,
    Each to each is dearest brother ;

Hues of the silken sheeny woof
  Momently shot into each other.
    All the mystery is thine ;
Smiling, frowning, evermore,
Thou art perfect in love-lore,
    Ever varying Madeline.

A subtle, sudden flame,
  By veering passion fann'd,
    About thee breaks and dances ;
  When I would kiss thy hand,
The flush of anger'd shame
    O'erflows thy calmer glances,
And o'er black brows drops down
A sudden-curved frown :
But when I turn away,
Thou, willing me to stay,
  Wooest not, nor vainly wranglest ;
    But, looking fixedly the while,
  All my bounding heart entanglest
    In a golden-netted smile ;
Then in madness and in bliss,
If my lips should dare to kiss
Thy taper fingers amorously,
Again thou blushest angerly ;
And o'er black brows drops down
A sudden-curved frown.

ISABEL.

Eyes not down-dropt nor over-bright, but fed
  With the clear-pointed flame of chastity,
Clear, without heat, undying, tended by
  Pure vestal thoughts in the translucent fane

Of her still spirit ; locks not wide-dispread,
   Madonna-wise on either side her head ;
    Sweet lips whereon perpetually did reign
  The summer calm of golden charity,
Were fixed shadows of thy fixed mood,
   Revered Isabel, the crown and head,
The stately flower of female fortitude,
   Of perfect wifehood and pure lowlihead.

The intuitive decision of a bright
  And thorough-edged intellect to part
    Error from crime ; a prudence to withhold ;
    The laws of marriage character'd in gold
  Upon the blanched tablets of her heart ;
A love still burning upward, giving light
To read those laws ; an accent very low
In blandishment, but a most silver flow
    Of subtle-paced counsel in distress,
Right to the heart and brain, tho' undescried,
    Winning its way with extreme gentleness
Thro' all the outworks of suspicious pride ;
A courage to endure and to obey ;
A hate of gossip parlance, and of sway,
Crown'd Isabel, thro' all her placid life,
The queen of marriage, a most perfect wife.

The mellow'd reflex of a winter moon ;
A clear stream flowing with a muddy one,
  Till in its onward current it absorbs
    With swifter movement and in purer light
      The vexed eddies of its wayward brother :
  A leaning and upbearing parasite,
    Clothing the stem, which else had fallen quite,
With cluster'd flower-bells and ambrosial orbs

Of rich fruit-bunches leaning on each other—
Shadow forth thee :—the world hath not another
(Though all her fairest forms are types of thee
And thou of God in thy great charity)
Of such a finish'd chasten'd purity.

THE BALLAD OF ORIANA.

My heart is wasted with my woe,
   Oriana.
There is no rest for me below,
   Oriana.
When the long dun wolds are ribb'd with snow,
And loud the Norland whirlwinds blow,
   Oriana,
Alone I wander to and fro,
   Oriana.

Ere the light on dark was growing,
   Oriana,
At midnight the cock was crowing,
   Oriana :
Winds were blowing, waters flowing
We heard the steeds to battle going,
   Oriana ;
Aloud the hollow bugle blowing,
   Oriana.

In the yew-wood black as night,
   Oriana,
Ere I rode into the fight,
   Oriana,
While blissful tears blinded my sight

By star-shine and by moonlight,
    Oriana,
I to thee my troth did plight,
    Oriana.

She stood upon the castle wall,
    Oriana :
She watch'd my crest among them all,
    Oriana :
She saw me fight, she heard me call,
When forth there stept a foeman tall,
    Oriana,
Atween me and the castle wall,
    Oriana.

The bitter arrow went aside,
    Oriana :
The false, false arrow went aside,
    Oriana :
The damned arrow glanced aside,
And pierced thy heart, my love, my bride,
    Oriana !
Thy heart, my life, my love, my bride,
    Oriana !

Oh ! narrow, narrow was the space,
    Oriana.
Loud, loud rung out the bugle's brays,
    Oriana.
Oh ! deathful stabs were dealt apace,
The battle deepen'd in its place,
    Oriana ;
But I was down upon my face,
    Oriana.

They should have stabb'd me where I lay,
    Oriana !
How could I rise and come away,
    Oriana ?
How could I look upon the day ?
They should have stabb'd me where I lay,
    Oriana—
They should have trod me into clay,
    Oriana.

O breaking heart that will not break,
    Oriana !
O pale, pale face so sweet and meek,
    Oriana !
Thou smilest, but thou dost not speak,
And then the tears run down my cheek,
    Oriana :
What wantest thou ? whom dost thou seek,
    Oriana ?

I cry aloud : none hear my cries,
    Oriana.
Thou comest atween me and the skies,
    Oriana.
I feel the tears of blood arise
Up from my heart unto my eyes,
    Oriana.
Within thy heart my arrow lies,
    Oriana.

O cursed hand ! O cursed blow !
    Oriana !
O happy thou that liest low,
    Oriana !

All night the silence seems to flow
Beside me in my utter woe,
          Oriana.
A weary, weary way I go,
          Oriana.

When Norland winds pipe down the sea,
          Oriana,
I walk, I dare not think of thee,
          Oriana.
Thou liest beneath the greenwood tree,
I dare not die and come to thee,
          Oriana.
I hear the roaring of the sea,
          Oriana.

MARIANA.

"Mariana in the moated grange."—*Measure for Measure.*

WITH blackest moss the flower-pots
    Were thickly crusted, one and all ;
The rusted nails fell from the knots
    That held the peach to the garden-wall.
The broken sheds look'd sad and strange :
    Unlifted was the clinking latch ;
    Weeded and worn the ancient thatch
Upon the lonely moated grange.
        She only said, " My life is dreary,
            He cometh not," she said ;
        She said, " I am aweary, aweary,
            I would that I were dead ! "

Her tears fell with the dews at even ;
   Her tears fell ere the dews were dried ;
She could not look on the sweet heaven,
   Either at morn or eventide.
After the flitting of the bats,
   When thickest dark did trance the sky,
   She drew her casement-curtain by,
And glanced athwart the glooming flats.
     She only said, " The night is dreary,
       He cometh not," she said ;
     She said, " I am aweary, aweary,
       I would that I were dead ! "

Upon the middle of the night,
   Waking she heard the night-fowl crow :
The cock sung out an hour ere light :
   From the dark fen the oxen's low
Came to her : without hope of change,
   In sleep she seem'd to walk forlorn,
   Till cold winds woke the gray-eyed morn
About the lonely moated grange.
     She only said, " The day is dreary,
       He cometh not," she said ;
     She said, " I am aweary, aweary,
       I would that I were dead ! "

About a stone-cast from the wall
   A sluice with blacken'd waters slept,
And o'er it many, round and small,
   The cluster'd marish-mosses crept.
Hard by a poplar shook alway,
   All silver-green with gnarled bark :
   For leagues no other tree did mark
The level waste, the rounding gray.

She only said, " My life is dreary,
    He cometh not," she said ;
She said, " I am aweary, aweary,
    I would that I were dead ! "

And ever when the moon was low,
    And the shrill winds were up and away,
In the white curtain, to and fro,
    She saw the gusty shadow sway.
But when the moon was very low,
    And wild winds bound within their cell,
    The shadow of the poplar fell
Upon her bed, across her brow.
        She only said, " The night is dreary,
            He cometh not," she said ;
        She said, " I am aweary, aweary,
            I would that I were dead ! "

All day within the dreamy house,
    The doors upon their hinges creak'd ;
The blue fly sung in the pane ; the mouse
    Behind the mouldering wainscot shriek'd,
Or from the crevice peer'd about.
    Old faces glimmer'd thro' the doors,
    Old footsteps trod the upper floors,
Old voices called her from without.
        She only said, " My life is dreary,
            He cometh not," she said ;
        She said, " I am aweary, aweary,
            I would that I were dead ! "

The sparrow's chirrup on the roof,
    The slow clock ticking, and the sound

Which to the wooing wind aloof
  The poplar made, did all confound
Her sense ; but most she loathed the hour
  When the thick-moted sunbeam lay
  Athwart the chambers, and the day
Was sloping toward his western bower.
    Then, said she, " I am very dreary,
      He will not come," she said ;
    She wept, " I am aweary, aweary,
      Oh God, that I were dead ! "

COME NOT, WHEN I AM DEAD.

COME not, when I am dead,
  To drop thy foolish tears upon my grave,
To trample round my fallen head,
  And vex the unhappy dust thou wouldst not save.
There let the wind sweep and the plover cry ;
      But thou, go by.

Child, if it were thine error or thy crime
  I care no longer, being all unblest :
Wed whom thou wilt, but I am sick of Time,
  And I desire to rest.
Pass on, weak heart, and leave me where I lie :
      Go by, go by.

ST. AGNES' EVE.

DEEP on the convent-roof the snows
  Are sparkling to the moon :
My breath to heaven like vapour goes :
  M y my soul follow soon !

The shadows of the convent-towers
   Slant down the snowy sward,
Still creeping with the creeping hours
   That lead me to my Lord:
Make Thou my spirit pure and clear
   As are the frosty skies,
Or this first snowdrop of the year
   That in my bosom lies.

As these white robes are soil'd and dark,
   To yonder shining ground ;
As this pale taper's earthly spark,
   To yonder argent round ;
So shows my soul before the Lamb,
   My spirit before Thee ;
So in mine earthly house I am,
   To that I hope to be.
Break up the heavens, O Lord ! and far,
   Thro' all yon starlight keen,
Draw me, Thy bride, a glittering star,
   In raiment white and clean.

He lifts me to the golden doors ;
   The flashes come and go ;
All heaven bursts her starry floors,
   And strows her lights below,
And deepens on and up ! the gates
   Roll back, and far within
For me the Heavenly Bridegroom waits,
   To make me pure of sin.
The sabbaths of Eternity,
   One sabbath deep and wide—
A light upon the shining sea—
   The Bridegroom with His bride !

RECOLLECTIONS OF THE ARABIAN
NIGHTS.

WHEN the breeze of a joyful dawn blew free
In the silken sail of infancy,
The tide of time flow'd back with me,
   The forward-flowing tide of time ;
And many a sheeny summer-morn,
Adown the Tigris I was borne,
By Bagdat's shrines of fretted gold,
High-walled gardens green and old ;
True Mussulman was I and sworn,
   For it was in the golden prime
      Of good Haroun Alraschid.

Anight my shallop, rustling thro'
The low and bloomed foliage, drove
The fragrant, glistening deeps, and clove
The citron-shadows in the blue :
By garden porches on the brim,
The costly doors flung open wide,
Gold glittering thro' lamplight dim,
And broider'd sofas on each side :
   In sooth it was a goodly time,
   For it was in the golden prime
      Of good Haroun Alraschid.

Often, where clear-stemm'd platans guard
The outlet, did I turn away
The boat-head down a broad canal
From the main river sluiced, where all
The sloping of the moon-lit sward
Was damask-work, and deep inlay

9

Of braided blooms unmown, which crept
Adown to where the water slept.
   A goodly place, a goodly time,
    For it was in the golden prime
      Of good Haroun Alraschid.

A motion from the river won
Ridged the smooth level, bearing on
My shallop thro' the star-strown calm,
Until another night in night
I enter'd, from the clearer light,
Imbower'd vaults of pillar'd palm,
Imprisoning sweets, which, as they clomb
Heavenward, were stay'd beneath the dome
   Of hollow boughs.— A goodly time,
    For it was in the golden prime
      Of good Haroun Alraschid.

Still onward ; and the clear canal
Is rounded to as clear a lake.
From the green rivage many a fall
Of diamond rillets musical,
Thro' little crystal arches low
Down from the central fountain's flow
Fall'n silver-chiming, seem'd to shake
The sparkling flints beneath the prow.
   A goodly place, a goodly time,
    For it was in the golden prime
      Of good Haroun Alraschid.

Above thro' many a bowery turn
A walk with vary-colour'd shells
Wander'd engrain'd.   On either side
All round about the fragrant marge
From fluted vase, and brazen urn

In order, eastern flowers large,
Some dropping low their crimson bells
Half-closed, and others studded wide
   With disks and tiars, fed the time
   With odour in the golden prime
     Of good Haroun Alraschid.

Far off, and where the lemon-grove
In closest coverture upsprung,
The living airs of middle night
Died round the bulbul as he sung ;
Not he : but something which possess'd
The darkness of the world, delight,
Life, anguish, death, immortal love,
Ceasing not, mingled, unrepress'd
   Apart from place, withholding time,
   But flattering the golden prime
     Of good Haroun Alraschid.

Black the garden-bowers and grots
Slumber'd : the solemn palms were ranged
Above, unwoo'd of summer wind :
A sudden splendour from behind
Flush'd all the leaves with rich gold-green,
And, flowing rapidly between
Their interspaces, counterchanged
The level lake with diamond-plots
   Of dark and bright.   A lovely time,
   For it was in the golden prime
     Of good Haroun Alraschid.

Dark-blue the deep sphere overhead,
Distinct with vivid stars inlaid,
Grew darker from that under-flame :
So, leaping lightly from the boat,

With silver anchor left afloat,
In marvel whence that glory came
Upon me, as in sleep I sank
In cool soft turf upon the bank,
    Entranced with that place and time,
    So worthy of the golden prime
        Of good Haroun Alraschid.

Thence thro' the garden I was drawn—
A realm of pleasance, many a mound,
And many a shadow-chequer'd lawn
Full of the city's stilly sound,
And deep myrrh-thickets blowing round
The stately cedar, tamarisks,
Thick rosaries of scented thorn,
Tall orient shrubs, and obelisks
    Graven with emblems of the time,
    In honour of the golden prime
        Of good Haroun Alraschid.

With dazed vision unawares
From the long alley's latticed shade
Emerged, I came upon the great
Pavilion of the Caliphat.
Right to the carven cedarn doors,
Flung inward over spangled floors,
Broad-baséd flights of marble stairs
Ran up with golden balustrade,
    After the fashion of the time,
    And humour of the golden prime
        Of good Haroun Alraschid.

The fourscore windows all alight
As with the quintessence of flame,

A million tapers flaring bright
From twisted silvers look'd to shame
The hollow-vaulted dark, and stream'd
Upon the mooned domes aloof
In inmost Bagdat, till there seem'd
Hundreds of crescents on the roof
    Of night new-risen, that marvellous time,
      To celebrate the golden prime
        Of good Haroun Alraschid.

Then stole I up, and trancedly
Gazed on the Persian girl alone,
Serene with argent-lidded eyes
Amorous, and lashes like to rays
Of darkness, and a brow of pearl
Tressed with redolent ebony,
In many a dark delicious curl,
Flowing beneath her rose-hued zone ;
    The sweetest lady of the time,
      Well worthy of the golden prime
        Of good Haroun Alraschid.

Six columns, three on either side,
Pure silver, underpropt a rich
Throne of the massive ore, from which
Down-droop'd, in many a floating fold,
Engarlanded and diaper'd
With inwrought flowers, a cloth of gold.
Thereon, his deep eye laughter-stirr'd
With merriment of kingly pride,
    Sole star of all that place and time,
      I saw him—in his golden prime,
        THE GOOD HAROUN ALRASCHID !

A DREAM OF FAIR WOMEN.

I READ, before my eyelids dropt their shade,
 " *The Legend of Good Women*," long ago
Sung by the morning star of song, who made
  His music heard below ;

Dan Chaucer, the first warbler, whose sweet breath
  Preluded those melodious bursts, that fill
The spacious times of great Elizabeth
  With sounds that echo still.

And, for a while, the knowledge of his art
  Held me above the subject, as strong gales
Hold swollen clouds from raining, tho' my heart,
  Brimful of those wild tales,

Charged both mine eyes with tears. In every land
  I saw, wherever light illumineth,
Beauty and anguish walking hand in hand
  The downward slope to death.

Those far-renowned brides of ancient song
  Peopled the hollow dark, like burning stars,
And I heard sounds of insult, shame, and wrong,
  And trumpets blown for wars ;

And clattering flints batter'd with clanging hoofs :
  And I saw crowds in column'd sanctuaries ;
And forms that pass'd at windows and on roofs
  Of marble palaces ;

Corpses across the threshold ; heroes tall
   Dislodging pinnacle and parapet
Upon the tortoise creeping to the wall ;
   Lances in ambush set ;

And high shrine-doors burst thro' with heated blasts
   That run before the fluttering tongues of fire ;
White surf wind-scatter'd over sails and masts,
   And ever climbing higher ;

Squadrons and squares of men in brazen plates,
   Scaffolds, still sheets of water, divers woes,
Ranges of glimmering vaults with iron grates,
   And hushed seraglios.

So shape chased shape as swift as, when to land
   Bluster the winds and tides the self-same way,
Crisp foam-flakes scud along the level sand,
   Torn from the fringe of spray.

I started once, or seem'd to start in pain,
   Resolved on noble things, and strove to speak,
As when a great thought strikes along the brain,
   And flushes all the cheek.

And once my arm was lifted to hew down
   A cavalier from off his saddle-bow,
That bore a lady from a leaguer'd town ;
   And then, I know not how,

All those sharp fancies, by down-lapsing thought
   Stream'd onward, lost their edges, and did creep
Roll'd on each other, rounded, smooth'd, and brought
   Into the gulfs of sleep.

At last methought that I had wander'd far
  In an old wood : fresh-wash'd in coolest dew
The maiden splendours of the morning star
  Shook in the stedfast blue.

Enormous elmtree-boles did stoop and lean
  Upon the dusky brushwood underneath
Their broad curved branches, fledged with clearest green,
  New from its silken sheath.

The dim red morn had died, her journey done,
  And with dead lips smiled at the twilight plain,
Half-fall'n across the threshold of the sun,
  Never to rise again.

There was no motion in the dumb dead air,
  Not any song of bird or sound of rill ;
Gross darkness of the inner sepulchre
  Is not so deadly still

As that wide forest.   Growths of jasmine turn'd
  Their humid arms festooning tree to tree,
And at the root thro' lush green grasses burn'd
  The red anemone.

I knew the flowers, I knew the leaves, I knew
  The tearful glimmer of the languid dawn
On those long, rank, dark wood-walks drench'd in dew,
  Leading from lawn to lawn.

The smell of violets, hidden in the green,
  Pour'd back into my empty soul and frame
The times when I remember to have been
  Joyful and free from blame.

And from within me a clear under-tone
    Thrill'd thro' mine ears in that unblissful clime
" Pass freely thro' : the wood is all thine own,
    Until the end of time."

At length I saw a lady within call,
    Stiller than chisell'd marble, standing there ;
A daughter of the gods, divinely tall,
    And most divinely fair.

Her loveliness with shame and with surprise
    Froze my swift speech ; she turning on my face
The star-like sorrows of immortal eyes,
    Spoke slowly in her place.

" I had great beauty : ask thou not my name :
    No one can be more wise than destiny.
Many drew swords and died.   Where'er I came
    I brought calamity."

" No marvel, sovereign lady : in fair field
    Myself for such a face had boldly died,"
I answer'd free ; and turning I appeal'd
    To one that stood beside.

But she, with sick and scornful looks averse,
    To her full height her stately stature draws ;
" My youth," she said, " was blasted with a curse :
    This woman was the cause.

" I was cut off from hope in that sad place,
    Which yet to name my spirit loathes and fears :
My father held his hand upon his face ;
    I, blinded with my tears,

"Still strove to speak : my voice was thick with sighs
  As in a dream.   Dimly I could descry
The stern black-bearded kings with wolfish eyes,
  Waiting to see me die.

" The high masts flicker'd as they lay afloat ;
  The crowds, the temples, waver'd, and the shore ;
The bright death quiver'd at the victim's throat ;
  Touch'd ; and I knew no more."

Whereto the other with a downward brow :
  " I would the white cold heavy-plunging foam,
Whirl'd by the wind, had roll'd me deep below,
  Then when I left my home."

Her slow full words sank thro' the silence drear,
  As thunder-drops fall on a sleeping sea :
Sudden I heard a voice that cried, " Come here
  That I may look on thee."

I turning saw, throned on a flowery rise,
  One sitting on a crimson scarf unroll'd ;
A queen, with swarthy cheeks and bold black eyes,
  Brow-bound with burning gold.

She, flashing forth a haughty smile, began :
  " I govern'd men by change, and so I sway'd
All moods.   'Tis long since I have seen a man.
  Once, like the moon, I made

" The ever-shifting currents of the blood
  According to my humour ebb and flow.
I have no men to govern in this wood :
  That makes my only woe.

" Nay—yet it chafes me that I could not bend
    One will ; nor tame and tutor with mine eye
That dull cold-blooded Cæsar.   Prythee, friend,
    Where is Mark Antony ?

" The man, my lover, with whom I rode sublime
    On Fortune's neck : we sat as God by God :
The Nilus would have risen before his time
    And flooded at our nod.

" We drank the Libyan Sun to sleep, and lit
    Lamps which out-burn'd Canopus.   O my life
In Egypt ! O the dalliance and the wit,
    The flattery and the strife,

" And the wild kiss, when fresh from war's alarms,
    My Hercules, my Roman Antony,
My mailed Bacchus leapt into my arms,
    Contented there to die !

" And there he died ; and when I heard my name
    Sigh'd forth with life I would not brook my fear
Of the other : with a worm I balk'd his fame.
    What else was left ? look here ! "

(With that she tore her robe apart, and half
    The polish'd argent of her breast to sight
Laid bare.   Thereto she pointed with a laugh,
    Showing the aspick's bite.)

" I died a Queen.   The Roman soldier found
    Me lying dead, my crown about my brows,
A name for ever !—lying robed and crown'd,
    Worthy a Roman spouse."

Her warbling voice, a lyre of widest range
   Struck by all passion, did fall down and glance
From tone to tone, and glided thro' all change
   Of liveliest utterance.

When she made pause I knew not for delight ;
   Because with sudden motion from the ground
She raised her piercing orbs, and fill'd with light
   The interval of sound.

Still with their fires Love tipt his keenest darts ;
   As once they drew into two burning rings
All beams of Love, melting the mighty hearts
   Of captains and of kings.

Slowly my sense undazzled.   Then I heard
   A noise of some one coming thro' the lawn,
And singing clearer than the crested bird,
   That claps his wings at dawn.

" The torrent brooks of hallow'd Israel
   From craggy hollows pouring, late and soon,
Sound all night long, in falling thro' the dell,
   Far-heard beneath the moon.

" The balmy moon of blessed Israel
   Floods all the deep-blue gloom with beams divine :
All night the splinter'd crags that wall the dell
   With spires of silver shine."

As one that museth where broad sunshine laves
   The lawn by some cathedral, thro' the door
Hearing the holy organ rolling waves
   Of sound on roof and floor

Within, and anthem sung, is charm'd and tied
  To where he stands,—so stood I, when that flow
Of music left the lips of her that died
  To save her father's vow ;

The daughter of the warrior Gileadite,
  A maiden pure ; as when she went along
From Mizpeh's tower'd gate with welcome light,
  With trimbrel and with song.

My words leapt forth : "Heaven heads the count of crimes
  With that wild oath."   She render'd answer high :
"Not so, nor once alone ; a thousand times
  I would be born and die.

"Single I grew, like some green plant, whose root
  Creeps to the garden water-pipes beneath,
Feeding the flower ; but ere my flower to fruit
  Changed, I was ripe for death.

"My God, my land, my father—these did move
  Me from my bliss of life, that Nature gave,
Lower'd softly with a threefold cord of love
  Down to a silent grave.

"And I went mourning, 'No fair Hebrew boy
  Shall smile away my maiden blame among
The Hebrew mothers'—emptied of all joy,
  Leaving the dance and song,

"Leaving the olive-gardens far below,
  Leaving the promise of my bridal bower,
The valleys of grape-loaded vines that glow
  Beneath the battled tower.

" The light white cloud swam over us.   Anon
   We heard the lion roaring from his den ;
We saw the large white stars rise one by one,
   Or, from the darken'd glen,

" Saw God divide the night with flying flame,
   And thunder on the everlasting hills.
I heard Him, for He spake, and grief became
   A solemn scorn of ills.

" When the next moon was roll'd into the sky,
   Strength came to me that equall'd my desire.
How beautiful a thing it was to die
   For God and for my sire !

" It comforts me in this one thought to dwell,
   That I subdued me to my father's will :
Because the kiss he gave me, ere I fell,
   Sweetens the spirit still.

" Moreover it is written that my race
   Hew'd Ammon, hip and thigh, from Aroer
On Arnon unto Minneth."   Here her face
   Glow'd, as I look'd at her.

She lock'd her lips : she left me where I stood :
   " Glory to God," she sang, and past afar,
Thridding the sombre boskage of the wood,
   Toward the morning-star.

Losing her carol I stood pensively,
   As one that from a casement leans his head,
When midnight bells cease ringing suddenly,
   And the old year is dead

" Alas ! alas ! " a low voice, full of care,
  Murmur'd beside me : " Turn and look on me :
I am that Rosamond, whom men call fair,
  If what I was I be.

" Would I had been some maiden coarse and poor !
  O me, that I should ever see the light !
Those dragon eyes of anger'd Eleanor
  Do hunt me, day and night."

She ceased in tears, fallen from hope and trust :
  To whom the Egyptian : " O, you tamely died !
You should have clung to Fulvia's waist, and thrust
  The dagger thro' her side."

With that sharp sound the white dawn's creeping beams,
  Stol'n to my brain, dissolved the mystery
Of folded sleep.   The captain of my dreams
  Ruled in the eastern sky.

Morn broaden'd on the borders of the dark,
  Ere I saw her, who clasped in her last trance
Her murder'd father's head, or Joan of Arc,
  A light of ancient France ;

Or her, who knew that Love can vanquish Death,
  Who kneeling, with one arm about her king,
Drew forth the poison with her balmy breath,
  Sweet as new buds in Spring.

No memory labours longer from the deep
  Gold-mines of thought to lift the hidden ore
That glimpses, moving up, than I from sleep
  To gather and tell o'er

Each little sound and sight.   With what dull pain
    Compassed, how eagerly I sought to strike
Into that wondrous track of dreams again !
    But no two dreams are like.

As when a soul laments, which hath been blest, .
    Desiring what is mingled with past years,
In yearnings that can never be exprest
    By signs or groans or tears ;

Because all words, tho' cull'd with choicest art,
    Failing to give the bitter of the sweet,
Wither beneath the palate, and the heart
    Faints, faded by its heat.

GODIVA.

I WAITED for the train at Coventry ;
I hung with grooms and porters on the bridge,
To watch the three tall spires ; and there I shaped
The city's ancient legend into this :—

Not only we, the latest seed of Time,
New men, that in the flying of a wheel
Cry down the past, not only we, that prate
Of rights and wrongs, have loved the people well,
And loathed to see them overtax'd ; but she
Did more, and underwent, and overcame,
The woman of a thousand summers back,
Godiva, wife to that grim Earl, who ruled
In Coventry : for when he laid a tax
Upon his town, and all the mothers brought
Their children, clamouring, " If we pay, we starve ! "
She sought her lord, and found him, where he strode

About the hall, among his dogs, alone,
His beard a foot before him, and his hair
A yard behind.   She told him of their tears,
And pray'd him, " If they pay this tax, they starve."
Whereat he stared, replying, half-amazed,
" You would not let your little finger ache
For such as *these?* "—" But I would die," said she.
He laugh'd, and swore by Peter and by Paul :
Then fillip'd at the diamond in her ear ;
" O ay, ay, ay, you talk ! "—" Alas ! " she said,
" But prove me what it is I would not do."
And from a heart as rough as Esau's hand,
He answer'd, " Ride you naked thro' the town,
And I repeal it ; " and nodding, as in scorn,
He parted, with great strides among his dogs.

So left alone, the passions of her mind,
As winds from all the compass shift and blow,
Made war upon each other for an hour,
Till pity won.   She sent a herald forth,
And bad him cry, with sound of trumpet, all
The hard condition ; but that she would loose
The people : therefore, as they loved her well,
From then till noon no foot should pace the street,
No eye look down, she passing ; but that all
Should keep within, door shut, and window barr'd.

Then fled she to her inmost bower, and there
Unclasp'd the wedded eagles of her belt,
The grim Earl's gift ; but ever at a breath
She linger'd, looking like a summer moon
Half-dipt in cloud : anon she shook her head,
And shower'd the rippled ringlets to her knee ;
Unclad herself in haste ; adown the stair

10

Stole on ; and, like a creeping sunbeam, slid
From pillar unto pillar, until she reach'd
The gateway ; there she found her palfrey trapt
In purple blazon'd with armorial gold.

Then she rode forth, clothed on with chastity :
The deep air listen'd round her as she rode,
And all the low wind hardly breathed for fear.
The little wide-mouth'd heads upon the spout
Had cunning eyes to see·: the barking cur
Made her cheek flame : her palfrey's footfall shot
Light horrors thro' her pulses : the blind walls
Were full of chinks and holes ; and overhead
Fantastic gables, crowding, stared : but she
Not less thro' all bore up, till, last, she saw
The white-flower'd elder-thicket from the field
Gleam thro' the Gothic archways in the wall.

Then she rode back, clothed on with chastity :
And one low churl, compact of thankless earth,
The fatal byword of all years to come,
Boring a little augur-hole in fear,
Peep'd—but his eyes, before they had their will,
Were shrivell'd into darkness in his head,
And dropt before him.   So the Powers, who wait
On noble deeds, cancell'd a sense misused ;
And she, that knew not, pass'd : and all at once,
With twelve great shocks of sound, the shameless noon
Was clash'd and hammer'd from a hundred towers,
One after one: but even then she gain'd
Her bower ; whence reissuing, robed and crown'd,
To meet her lord, she took the tax away,
And built herself an everlasting name.

THE CHARGE OF THE LIGHT BRIGADE.

HALF a league, half a league,
Half a league onward,
All in the valley of Death
    Rode the six hundred.
" Forward, the Light Brigade,
Charge for the guns ! " he said
Into the valley of Death
    Rode the six hundred.

" Forward, the Light Brigade ! "
Was there a man dismay'd ?
Not tho' the soldier knew
    Some one had blunder'd.
Theirs not to make reply,
Theirs not to reason why,
Theirs but to do and die.
Into the valley of Death
    Rode the six hundred.

Cannon to right of them,
Cannon to left of them,
Cannon in front of them
    Volley'd and thunder'd ;
Stormed at with shot and shell,
Boldly they rode and well,
Into the jaws of Death,
Into the mouth of Hell
    Rode the six hundred.

Flash'd all their sabres bare,
Flash'd as they turned in air,
Sabring the gunners there,
Charging an army, while
    All the world wonder'd ;
Plunged in the battery smoke
Right thro' the line they broke,
Cossack and Russian
Reel'd from the sabre stroke
    Shatter'd and sunder'd.
Then they rode back, but not—
    Not the six hundred.

Cannon to right of them,
Cannon to left of them,
Cannon behind them
    Volley'd and thunder'd ;
Storm'd at with shot and shell,
While horse and hero fell,
They that had fought so well
Came thro' the jaws of Death
Back from the mouth of Hell,
All that was left of them,
    Left of six hundred.

When can their glory fade ?
O, the wild charge they made !
    All the world wonder'd.
Honour the charge they made !
Honour the Light Brigade,
    Noble six hundred !

ODE ON THE DEATH OF THE DUKE OF WELLINGTON.

BURY the Great Duke
  With an empire's lamentation,
Let us bury the Great Duke
  To the noise of the mourning of a mighty nation,
Mourning when their leaders fall,
Warriors carry the warrior's pall,
And sorrow darkens hamlet and hall.

Where shall we lay the man whom we deplore ?
Here, in streaming London's central roar.
Let the sound of those he wrought for,
And the feet of those he fought for,
Echo round his bones for evermore.

Lead out the pageant: sad and slow,
As fits an universal woe,
Let the long long procession go,
And let the sorrowing crowd about it grow,
And let the mournful martial music blow ;
The last great Englishman is low.

Mourn, for to us he seems the last,
Remembering all his greatness in the Past.
No more in soldier fashion will he greet
With lifted hand the gazer in the street.
O friends, our chief state-oracle is mute :
Mourn for the man of long-enduring blood,
The statesman-warrior, moderate, resolute,
Whole in himself, a common good.
Mourn for the man of amplest influence,

Yet clearest of ambitious crime,
Our greatest yet with least pretence,
Great in council and great in war,
Foremost captain of his time,
Rich in saving common-sense,
And, as the greatest only are,
In his simplicity sublime.
O good gray head which all men knew,
O voice from which their omens all men drew,
O iron nerve to true occasion true,
O fall'n at length that tower of strength
Which stood four-square to all the winds that blew !
Such was he whom we deplore.
The long self-sacrifice of life is o'er.
The great World-victor's victor will be seen no more.

All is over and done :
Render thanks to the Giver,
England, for thy son.
Let the bell be toll'd.
Render thanks to the Giver,
And render him to the mould.
Under the cross of gold
That shines over city and river,
There shall he rest for ever
Among the wise and the bold.
Let the bell be toll'd :
And a reverent people behold
The towering car, the sable steeds :
Bright let it be with its blazon'd deeds,
Dark in its funeral fold.
Let the bell be toll'd :
And a deeper knell in the heart be knoll'd ;

And the sound of the sorrowing anthem roll'd
Thro' the dome of the golden cross ;
And the volleying cannon thunder his loss ;
He knew their voices of old.
For many a time in many a clime
His captain's-ear has heard them boom
Bellowing victory, bellowing doom ;
When he with those deep voices wrought,
Guarding realms and kings from shame ;
With those deep voices our dead captain taught
The tyrant, and asserts his claim
In that dread sound to the great name,
Which he has won so pure of blame,
In praise and in dispraise the same,
A man of well-attemper'd frame.
O civic muse, to such a name,
To such a name for ages long,
To such a name,
Preserve a broad approach of fame,
And ever-ringing avenues of song.

Who is he that cometh, like an honour'd guest,
With banner and with music, with soldier and with
    priest,
With a nation weeping, and breaking on my rest?
Mighty seaman, this is he
Was great by land as thou by sea.
Thine island loves thee well, thou famous man,
The greatest sailor since our world began.
Now, to the roll of muffled drums,
To thee the greatest soldier comes ;
For this is he
Was great by land as thou by sea ;

His foes were thine ; he kept us free ;
O give him welcome, this is he,
Worthy of our gorgeous rites,
And worthy to be laid by thee ;
For this is England's greatest son,
He that gain'd a hundred fights,
Nor ever lost an English gun ;
This is he that far away
Against the myriads of Assaye
Clash'd with his fiery few and won ;
And underneath another sun,
Warring on a later day,
Round affrighted Lisbon drew
The treble works, the vast designs
Of his labour'd rampart-lines,
Where he greatly stood at bay,
Whence he issued forth anew,
And ever great and greater grew,
Beating from the wasted vines
Back to France her banded swarms,
Back to France with countless blows,
Till o'er the hills her eagles flew
Past the Pyrenean pines,
Follow'd up in valley and glen
With blare of bugle, clamour of men,
Roll of cannon and clash of arms,
And England pouring on her foes.
Such a war had such a close.
Again their ravening eagle rose
In anger, wheel'd on Europe-shadowing wings,
And barking for the thrones of kings ;
Till one that sought but Duty's iron crown
On that loud sabbath shook the spoiler down ;

A day of onsets of despair !
Dash'd on every rocky square
Their surging charges foam'd themselves away ;
Last, the Prussian trumpet blew ;
Thro' the long-tormented air
Heaven flash'd a sudden jubilant ray,
And down we swept and charged and overthrew.
So great a soldier taught us there,
What long-enduring hearts could do
In that world's-earthquake, Waterloo !
Mighty seaman, tender and true,
And pure as he from taint of craven guile,
O saviour of the silver-coasted isle,
O shaker of the Baltic and the Nile,
If aught of things that here befall
Touch a spirit among things divine,
If love of country move thee there at all,
Be glad, because his bones are laid by thine !
And thro' the centuries let a people's voice
In full acclaim,
A people's voice,
The proof and echo of all human fame,
A people's voice, when they rejoice
At civic revel and pomp and game,
Attest their great commander's claim
With honour, honour, honour, honour to him,
Eternal honour to his name.

A people's voice ! we are a people yet.
Tho' all men else their nobler dreams forget
Confused by brainless mobs and lawless Powers;
Thank Him who isled us here, and roughly set
His Saxon in blown seas and storming showers,

We have a voice, with which to pay the debt
Of boundless love and reverence and regret
To those great men who fought, and kept it ours.
And keep it ours, O God, from brute control ;
O Statesmen, guard us, guard the eye, the soul
Of Europe, keep our noble England whole,
And save the one true seed of freedom sown
Betwixt a people and their ancient throne,
That sober freedom out of which there springs
Our loyal passion for our temperate kings ;
For, saving that, ye help to save mankind
Till public wrong be crumbled into dust,
And drill the raw world for the march of mind,
Till crowds at length be sane and crowns be just.
But wink no more in slothful overtrust.
Remember him who led your hosts ;
He bad you guard the sacred coasts.
Your cannons moulder on the seaward wall ;
His voice is silent in your council-hall
For ever ; and whatever tempests lour
For ever silent ; even if they broke
In thunder, silent ; yet remember all
He spoke among you, and the Man who spoke ;
Who never sold the truth to serve the hour,
Nor palter'd with Eternal God for power ;
Who let the turbid streams of rumour flow
Thro' either babbling world of high and low ;
Whose life was work, whose language rife
With rugged maxims hewn from life ;
Who never spoke against a foe ;
Whose eighty winters freeze with one rebuke
All great self-seekers trampling on the right :
Truth-teller was our England's Alfred named ;

Truth-lover was our English Duke ;
Whatever record leap to light
He never shall be shamed.

Lo, the leader in these glorious wars
Now to glorious burial slowly borne,
Follow'd by the brave of other lands,
He, on whom from both her open hands
Lavish Honour shower'd all her stars,
And affluent Fortune emptied all her horn.
Yea, let all good things await
Him who cares not to be great,
But as he saves or serves the state.
Not once or twice in our rough island-story,
The path of duty was the way to glory :
He that walks it, only thirsting
For the right, and learns to deaden
Love of self, before his journey closes,
He shall find the stubborn thistle bursting
Into glossy purples, which outredden
All voluptuous garden-roses.
Not once or twice in our fair island-story,
The path of duty was the way to glory :
He, that ever following her commands,
On with toil of heart and knees and hands,
Thro' the long gorge to the far light has won
His path upward, and prevail'd,
Shall find the toppling crags of Duty scaled
Are close upon the shining table-lands
To which our God Himself is moon and sun.
Such was he : his work is done.
But while the races of mankind endure,
Let his great example stand

Colossal, seen of every land,
And keep the soldier firm, the statesman pure ;
Till in all lands and thro' all human story
The path of duty be the way to glory :
And let the land whose hearths he saved from shame
For many and many an age proclaim
At civic revel and pomp and game,
And when the long-illumined cities flame,
Their ever-loyal iron leader's fame,
With honour, honour, honour, honour to him,
Eternal honour to his name.

Peace, his triumph will be sung
By some yet unmoulded tongue
Far on in summers that we shall not see :
Peace, it is a day of pain
For one about whose patriarchal knee
Late the little children clung :
O peace, it is a day of pain
For one, upon whose hand and heart and brain
Once the weight and fate of Europe hung.
Ours the pain, be his the gain !
More than is of man's degree
Must be with us, watching here
At this, our great solemnity.
Whom we see not we revere,
We revere, and we refrain
From talk of battles loud and vain,
And brawling memories all too free
For such a wise humility
As befits a solemn fane :
We revere, and while we hear
The tides of Music's golden sea

Setting toward eternity,
Uplifted high in heart and hope are we,
Until we doubt not that for one so true
There must be other nobler work to do
Than when he fought at Waterloo,
And Victor he must ever be.
For tho' the Giant Ages heave the hill
And break the shore, and evermore
Make and break, and work their will ;
Tho' world on world in myriad myriads roll
Round us, each with different powers,
And other forms of life than ours,
What know we greater than the soul ?
On God and Godlike men we build our trust.

Hush, the Dead March wails in the people's ears :
The dark crowd moves, and there are sobs and tears :
The black earth yawns : the mortal disappears ;
Ashes to ashes, dust to dust ;
He is gone who seem'd so great.—
Gone ; but nothing can bereave him
Of the force he made his own
Being here, and we believe him
Something far advanced in State,
And that he wears a truer crown
Than any wreath that man can weave him.
But speak no more of his renown,
Lay your earthly fancies down,
And in the vast cathedral leave him.
God accept him, Christ receive him.

THE LADY OF SHALOTT.

PART I.

On either side the river lie
Long fields of barley and of rye,
That clothe the wold and meet the sky;
And thro' the field the road runs by
      To many-tower'd Camelot;
And up and down the people go,
Gazing where the lilies blow
Round an island there below,
      The island of Shalott.

Willows whiten, aspens quiver,
Little breezes dusk and shiver
Thro' the wave that runs for ever
By the island in the river
      Flowing down to Camelot.
Four gray walls, and four gray towers,
Overlook a space of flowers,
And the silent isle imbowers
      The Lady of Shalott.

By the margin, willow-veil'd,
Slide the heavy barges trail'd
By slow horses; and unhail'd
The shallop flitteth silken sail'd
      Skimming down to Camelot:
But who hath seen her wave her hand?
Or at the casement seen her stand?
Or is she known in all the land,
      The Lady of Shalott?

Only reapers, reaping early
In among the bearded barley,
Hear a song that echoes cheerly
From the river winding clearly,
          Down to tower'd Camelot :
And by the moon the reaper weary,
Piling sheaves in uplands airy,
Listening, whispers " 'Tis the fairy
          Lady of Shalott."

PART II.

THERE she weaves by night and day
A magic web with colours gay.
She has heard a whisper say,
A curse is on her if she stay
          To look down to Camelot.
She knows not what the curse may be,
And so she weaveth steadily,
And little other care hath she,
          The Lady of Shalott.

And moving thro' a mirror clear
That hangs before her all the year,
Shadows of the world appear.
There she sees the highway near
          Winding down to Camelot :
There the river eddy whirls,
And there the surly village-churls,
And the red cloaks of market girls,
          Pass onward from Shalott.

Sometimes a troop of damsels glad,
An abbot on an ambling pad,
Sometimes a curly shepherd-lad,
Or long-hair'd page in crimson clad,
        Goes by to tower'd Camelot ;
And sometimes thro' the mirror blue
The knights come riding two and two :
She hath no loyal knight and true,
        The Lady of Shalott.

But in her web she still delights
To weave the mirror's magic sights,
For often thro' the silent nights
A funeral, with plumes and lights,
        And music, went to Camelot :
Or when the moon was overhead,
Came two young lovers lately wed ;
" I am half-sick of shadows," said
        The Lady of Shalott.

Part III.

A bow-shot from her bower-eaves,
He rode between the barley-sheaves,
The sun came dazzling thro' the leaves,
And flamed upon the brazen greaves
        Of bold Sir Lancelot.
A red-cross knight for ever kneel'd
To a lady in his shield,
That sparkled on the yellow field,
        Beside remote Shalott.

The gemmy bridle glitter'd free,
Like to some branch of stars we see

Hung in the golden Galaxy.
The bridle bells rang merrily
        As he rode down to Camelot :
And from his blazon'd baldric slung
A mighty silver bugle hung,
And as he rode his armour rung,
        Beside remote Shalott.

All in the blue unclouded weather
Thick-jewell'd shone the saddle-leather,
The helmet and the helmet-feather
Burn'd like one burning flame together,
        As he rode down to Camelot.
As often thro' the purple night,
Below the starry clusters bright,
Some bearded meteor, trailing light,
        Moves over still Shalott.

His broad clear brow in sunlight glow'd ;
On burnish'd hooves his war-horse trode ;
From underneath his helmet flow'd
His coal-black curls as on he rode,
        As he rode down to Camelot.
From the bank and from the river
He flash'd into the crystal mirror,
" Tirra lirra," by the river
        Sang Sir Lancelot.

She left the web, she left the loom,
She made three paces thro' the room,
She saw the water-lily bloom,
She saw the helmet and the plume,
        She look'd down to Camelot.

Out flew the web and floated wide ;
The mirror crack'd from side to side ;
" The curse is come upon me," cried
   The Lady of Shalott.

Part IV.

In the stormy east-wind straining,
The pale yellow woods were waning,
The broad stream in his banks complaining,
Heavily the low sky raining
   Over tower'd Camelot ;
Down she came and found a boat
Beneath a willow left afloat,
And round about the prow she wrote
   The Lady of Shalott.

And down the river's dim expanse—
Like some bold seër in a trance,
Seeing all his own mischance—
With a glassy countenance
   Did she look to Camelot.
And at the closing of the day
She loosed the chain, and down she lay ;
The broad stream bore her far away,
   The Lady of Shalott.

Lying, robed in snowy white
That loosely flew to left and right—
The leaves upon her falling light—
Thro' the noises of the night
   She floated down to Camelot :

And as the boat-head wound along
The willowy hills and fields among,
They heard her singing her last song,
        The Lady of Shalott.

Heard a carol, mournful, holy,
Chanted loudly, chanted lowly,
Till her blood was frozen slowly,
And her eyes were darken'd wholly,
        Turn'd to tower'd Camelot;
For ere she reach'd upon the tide
The first house by the water-side,
Singing in her song she died,
        The Lady of Shalott.

Under tower and balcony,
By garden-wall and gallery,
A gleaming shape she floated by,
Dead-pale between the houses high,
        Silent into Camelot.
Out upon the wharfs they came,
Knight and burgher, lord and dame,
And round the prow they read her name,
        The Lady of Shalott.

Who is this? and what is here?
And in the lighted palace near
Died the sound of royal cheer;
And they cross'd themselves for fear,
        All the knights at Camelot:
But Lancelot mused a little space;
He said, "She has a lovely face;
God in His mercy lend her grace,
        The Lady of Shalott."

SIR GALAHAD.

My good blade carves the casques of men,
    My tough lance thrusteth sure,
My strength is as the strength of ten,
    Because my heart is pure.
The shattering trumpet shrilleth high,
    The hard brands shiver on the steel,
The splinter'd spear-shafts crack and fly,
    The horse and rider reel :
They reel, they roll in clanging lists,
    And when the tide of combat stands,
Perfume and flowers fall in showers,
    That lightly rain from ladies' hands.

How sweet are looks that ladies bend
    On whom their favours fall !
For them I battle till the end,
    To save from shame and thrall :
But all my heart is drawn above,
    My knees are bow'd in crypt and shrine :
I never felt the kiss of love,
    Nor maiden's hand in mine.
More bounteous aspects on me beam,
    Me mightier transports move and thrill ;
So keep I fair thro' faith and prayer
    A virgin heart in work and will.

When down the stormy crescent goes,
    A light before me swims,
Between dark stems the forest glows,
    I hear a noise of hymns :

Then by some secret shrine I ride ;
  I hear a voice, but none are there ;
The stalls are void, the doors are wide,
  The tapers burning fair.
Fair gleams the snowy altar-cloth,
  The silver vessels sparkle clean,
The shrill bell rings, the censer swings,
  And solemn chaunts resound between.

Sometimes on lonely mountain-meres
  I find a magic bark ;
I leap on board : no helmsman steers :
  I float till all is dark.
A gentle sound, an awful light !
  Three angels bear the holy Grail :
With folded feet, in stoles of white,
  On sleeping wings they sail.
Ah, blessed vision ! blood of God !
  My spirit beats her mortal bars,
As down dark tides the glory slides,
  And star-like mingles with the stars.

When on my goodly charger borne
  Thro' dreaming towns I go,
The cock crows ere the Christmas morn,
  The streets are dumb with snow.
The tempest crackles on the leads,
  And, ringing, spins from brand and mail ;
But o'er the dark a glory spreads,
  And gilds the driving hail.
I leave the plain, I climb the height ;
  No branchy thicket shelter yields ;
But blessed forms in whistling storms
  Fly o'er waste fens and windy fields.

A maiden knight—to me is given
　　Such hope, I know not fear ;
I yearn to breathe the airs of heaven
　　That often meet me here.
I muse on joy that will not cease,
　　Pure spaces clothed in living beams,
Pure lilies of eternal peace,
　　Whose odours haunt my dreams ;
And, stricken by an angel's hand,
　　This mortal armour that I wear,
This weight and size, this heart and eyes,
　　Are touch'd, are turn'd to finest air.

The clouds are broken in the sky,
　　And thro' the mountain-walls
A rolling organ-harmony
　　Swells up, and shakes and falls.
Then move the trees, the copses nod,
　　Wings flutter, voices hover clear :
" O just and faithful knight of God !
　　Ride on ! the prize is near."
So pass I hostel, hall, and grange ;
　　By bridge and ford, by park and pale,
All-arm d I ride, whate'er betide,
　　Until I find the holy Grail.

MORTE D'ARTHUR.

So all day long the noise of battle roll'd
Among the mountains by the winter sea ;
Until King Arthur's table, man by man,
Had fall'n in Lyonness about their Lord,
King Arthur : then, because his wound was deep,

The bold Sir Bedivere uplifted him,
Sir Bedivere, the last of all his knights,
And bore him to a chapel nigh the field,
A broken chancel with a broken cross,
That stood on a dark strait of barren land.
On one side lay the Ocean, and on one
Lay a great water, and the moon was full.

Then spake King Arthur to Sir Bedivere :
" The sequel of to-day unsolders all
The goodliest fellowship of famous knights
Whereof this world holds record.   Such a sleep
They sleep—the men I loved.   I think that we
Shall never more, at any future time,
Delight our souls with talk of knightly deeds,
Walking about the gardens and the halls
Of Camelot, as in the days that were.
I perish by this people which I made,—
Tho' Merlin sware that I should come again
To rule once more—but let what will be, be,
I am so deeply smitten thro' the helm
That without help I cannot last till morn.
Thou therefore take my brand Excalibur,
Which was my pride : for thou rememberest how
In those old days, one summer noon, an arm
Rose up from out the bosom of the lake,
Clothed in white samite, mystic, wonderful,
Holding the sword—and how I row'd across
And took it, and have worn it, like a king :
And, wheresoever I am sung or told
In aftertime, this also shall be known :
But now delay not : take Excalibur,
And fling him far into the middle mere :
Watch what thou seëst, and lightly bring me word."

To him replied the bold Sir Bedivere:
"It is not meet, Sir King, to leave thee thus,
Aidless, alone, and smitten thro' the helm.
A little thing may harm a wounded man.
Yet I thy hest will all perform at full,
Watch what I see, and lightly bring thee word."

So saying, from the ruin'd shrine he stept
And in the moon athwart the place of tombs,
Where lay the mighty bones of ancient men,
Old knights, and over them the sea-wind sang
Shrill, chill, with flakes of foam.   He, stepping down
By zig-zag paths, and juts of pointed rock,
Came on the shining levels of the lake.
There drew he forth the brand Excalibur,
And o'er him, drawing it, the winter moon,
Brightening the skirts of a long cloud, ran forth
And sparkled keen with frost against the hilt:
For all the haft twinkled with diamond sparks,
Myriads of topaz-lights, and jacinth-work
Of subtlest jewellery.   He gazed so long
That both his eyes were dazzled, as he stood,
This way and that dividing the swift mind,
In act to throw: but at the last it seem'd
Better to leave Excalibur conceal'd
There in the many-knotted waterflags,
That whistled stiff and dry about the marge.
So strode he back slow to the wounded king.

Then spake King Arthur to Sir Bedivere:
"Hast thou perform'd my mission which I gave?
What is it thou hast seen? or what hast heard?"
And answer made the bold Sir Bedivere:
"I heard the ripple washing in the reeds,
And the wild water lapping on the crag."

To whom replied King Arthur, faint and pale :
" Thou hast betray'd thy nature and thy name,
Not rendering true answer, as beseem'd
Thy fëalty, nor like a noble knight :
For surer sign had follow'd, either hand,
Or voice, or else a motion of the mere.
This is a shameful thing for men to lie.
Yet now, I charge thee, quickly go again
As thou art lief and dear, and do the thing
I bad thee, watch, and lightly bring me word."

Then went Sir Bedivere the second time
Across the ridge, and paced beside the mere,
Counting the dewy pebbles, fix'd in thought ;
But when he saw the wonder of the hilt,
How curiously and strangely chased, he smote
His palms together, and he cried aloud.
" And if indeed I cast the brand away,
Surely a precious thing, one worthy note,
Should thus be lost for ever from the earth,
Which might have pleased the eyes of many men.
What good should follow this, if this were done ?
What harm, undone ? deep harm to disobey,
Seeing obedience is the bond of rule.
Were it well to obey then, if a king demand
An act unprofitable, against himself ?
The King is sick, and knows not what he does.
What record, or what relic of my lord
Should be to aftertime, but empty breath
And rumours of a doubt ? but were this kept,
Stored in some treasure-house of mighty kings,
Some one might show it at a joust of arms,
Saying, ' King Arthur's sword, Excalibur,
Wrought by the lonely maiden of the Lake.
Nine years she wrought it, sitting in the deeps

Upon the hidden bases of the hills.'
So might some old man speak in the aftertime
To all the people, winning reverence.
But now much honour and much fame were lost."
So spake he, clouded with his own conceit,
And hid Excalibur the second time,
And so strode back slow to the wounded King.

    Then spoke King Arthur, breathing heavily :
"What is it thou hast seen ? or what hast heard?"
And answer made the bold Sir Bedivere :
" I heard the water lapping on the crag,
And the long ripple washing in the reeds."
To whom replied King Arthur, much in wrath :
" Ah, miserable and unkind, untrue,
Unknightly, traitor-hearted !   Woe is me !
Authority forgets a dying king,
Laid widow'd of the power in his eye
That bow'd the will.   I see thee what thou art,
For thou, the latest-left of all my knights,
In whom should meet the offices of all,
Thou wouldst betray me for the precious hilt ;
Either from lust of gold, or like a girl
Valuing the giddy pleasure of the eyes.
Yet, for a man may fail in duty twice,
And the third time may prosper, get thee hence :
But, if thou spare to fling Excalibur,
I will arise and slay thee with my hands."

    Then quickly rose Sir Bedivere, and ran,
And, leaping down the ridges lightly, plunged
Among the bulrush-beds, and clutch'd the sword,
And strongly wheel'd and threw it.   The great brand
Made lightnings in the splendour of the moon,
And flashing round and round, and whirl'd in an arch,

Shot like a streamer of the northern morn,
Seen where the moving isles of winter shock
By night, with noises of the northern sea.
So flash'd and fell the brand Excalibur :
But ere he dipt the surface, rose an arm
Clothed in white samite, mystic, wonderful,
And caught him by the hilt, and brandish'd him
Three times, and drew him under in the mere.
And lightly went the other to the King.

　　Then spoke King Arthur, drawing thicker breath :
" Now see I by thine eyes that this is done.
Speak out : what is it thou hast heard, or seen ? "
And answer made the bold Sir Bedivere :
" Sir King, I closed mine eyelids, lest the gems
Should blind my purpose, for I never saw,
Nor shall see, here or elsewhere, till I die,
Not tho' I live three lives of mortal men,
So great a miracle as yonder hilt.
Then with both hands I flung him, wheeling him ;
But when I look'd again, behold an arm,
Clothed in white samite, mystic, wonderful,
That caught him by the hilt, and brandish'd him
Three times, and drew him under in the mere."
And answer made King Arthur, breathing hard :
" My end draws nigh ; 'tis time that I were gone.
Make broad thy shoulders to receive my weight,
And bear me to the margin ; yet I fear
My wound hath taken cold, and I shall die."

　　So saying, from the pavement he half rose,
Slowly, with pain, reclining on his arm,
And looking wistfully with wide blue eyes
As in a picture.　Him Sir Bedivere
Remorsefully regarded thro' his tears,
And would have spoken, but he found not words,

Then took with care, and kneeling on one knee,
O'er both his shoulders drew the languid hands,
And rising bore him thro' the place of tombs.

But, as he walk'd, King Arthur panted hard,
Like one that feels a nightmare on his bed
When all the house is mute.   So sigh'd the King,
Muttering and murmuring at his ear " Quick, quick !
I fear it is too late, and I shall die."
But the other swiftly strode from ridge to ridge,
Clothed with his breath, and looking, as he walk'd
Larger than human on the frozen hills.
He heard the deep behind him, and a cry
Before.   His own thought drove him like a goad.
Dry clash'd his harness in the icy caves
And barren chasms, and all to left and right
The bare black cliff clang'd round him, as he based
His feet on juts of slippery crag that rang
Sharp-smitten with the dint of armed heels—
And on a sudden, lo ! the level lake,
And the long glories of the winter moon.

Then saw they how there hove a dusky barge,
Dark as a funeral scarf from stem to stern,
Beneath them ; and descending they were ware
That all the decks were dense with stately forms
Black-stoled, black-hooded, like a dream—by these
Three Queens with crowns of gold—and from them rose
A cry that shiver'd to the tingling stars,
And, as it were one voice, an agony
Of lamentation, like a wind, that shrills
All night in a waste land, where no one comes,
Or hath come, since the making of the world.

Then murmur'd Arthur, " Place me in the barge,"

And to the barge they came. There those three Queens
Put forth their hands, and took the King and wept.
But she, that rose the tallest of them all
And fairest, laid his head upon her lap,
And loosed the shatter'd casque, and chafed his hands,
And call'd him by his name, complaining loud,
And dropping bitter tears against his brow
Striped with dark blood : for all his face was white
And colourless, and like the wither'd moon
Smote by the fresh beam of the springing east ;
And all his greaves and cuisses dash'd with drops
Of onset ; and the light and lustrous curls—
That made his forehead like a rising sun
High from the däis-throne—were parch'd with dust ;
Or, clotted into points and hanging loose,
Mix'd with the knightly growth that fringed his lips.
So like a shatter'd column lay the King ;
Not like that Arthur who, with lance in rest,
From spur to plume a star of tournament,
Shot thro' the lists at Camelot, and charged
Before the eyes of ladies and of kings.

Then loudly cried the bold Sir Bedivere,
" Ah ! my Lord Arthur, whither shall I go ?
Where shall I hide my forehead and my eyes ?
For now I see the true old times are dead,
When every morning brought a noble chance,
And every chance brought out a noble knight.
Such times have been not since the light that led
The holy Elders with the gift of myrrh.
But now the whole ROUND TABLE is dissolved
Which was an image of the mighty world ;
And I, the last, go forth companionless,
And the days darken round me, and the years,
Among new men, strange faces, other minds."

And slowly answer'd Arthur from the barge :
" The old order changeth, yielding place to new,
And God fulfils Himself in many ways,
Lest one good custom should corrupt the world.
Comfort thyself : what comfort is in me ?
I have lived my life, and that which I have done
May He within himself make pure ! but thou,
If thou shouldst never see my face again,
Pray for my soul.   More things are wrought by prayer
Than this world dreams of.   Wherefore, let thy voice
Rise like a fountain for me night and day.
For what are men better than sheep or goats
That nourish a blind life within the brain,
If, knowing God, they lift not hands of prayer
Both for themselves and those who call them friend ?
For so the whole round earth is every way
Bound by gold chains about the feet of God.
But now farewell.   I am going a long way
With these thou seëst—if indeed I go—
(For all my mind is clouded with a doubt)
To the island-valley of Avilion ;
Where falls not hail, or rain, or any snow,
Nor ever wind blows loudly ; but it lies
Deep-meadow'd, happy, fair with orchard-lawns
And bowery hollows crown'd with summer sea,
Where I will heal me of my grievous wound."

So said he, and the barge with oar and sail
Moved from the brink, like some full-breasted swan
That, fluting a wild carol ere her death,
Ruffles her pure cold plume, and takes the flood
With swarthy webs.   Long stood Sir Bedivere
Revolving many memories, till the hull
Look'd one black dot against the verge of dawn,
And on the mere the wailing died away.

MAUD ; A MONODRAMA.

I.

I HATE the dreadful hollow behind the little
      wood,
Its lips in the field above are dabbled with blood-red
      heath,
The red-ribb'd ledges drip with a silent horror
      of blood,
And Echo there, whatever is ask'd her, answers
      " Death."

For there in the ghastly pit long since a body was
      found,
His who had given me life—O father ! O God !
      was it well ?—
Mangled, and flatten'd, and crush'd, and dinted into
      the ground :
There yet lies the rock that fell with him when
      he fell.

Did he fling himself down ? who knows ? for a
      vast speculation had fail'd,
And ever he mutter'd and madden'd, and ever
      wann'd with despair,
And out he walk'd when the wind like a broken
      worldling wail'd,
And the flying gold of the ruin'd woodlands drove
      thro' the air.

I remember the time, for the roots of my hair
    were stirr'd
By a shuffled step, by a dead weight trail'd, by a
    whisper'd fright,
And my pulses closed their gates with a shock on
    my heart as I heard
The shrill-edged shriek of a mother divide the
    shuddering night.

Villainy somewhere! whose? One says, we are
    villains all.
Not he : his honest fame should at least by me be
    maintain'd :
But that old man, now lord of the broad estate and
    the Hall,
Dropt off gorged from a scheme that had left us
    flaccid and drain'd.

Why do they prate of the blessings of Peace? we
    have made them a curse,
Pickpockets, each hand lusting for all that is not
    its own ;
And lust of gain, in the spirit of Cain, is it better
    or worse
Than the heart of the citizen hissing in war on
    his own hearthstone ?

But these are the days of advance, the works of the
    men of mind,
When who but a fool would have faith in a trades-
    man's ware or his word ?
Is it peace or war? Civil war, as I think, and that
    of a kind
The viler, as underhand, not openly bearing the
    sword.

Sooner or later I too may passively take the
    print
Of the golden age—why not ? I have neither hope
    nor trust ;
May make my heart as a millstone, set my face as
    a flint,
Cheat and be cheated, and die : who knows ? we
    are ashes and dust.

Peace sitting under her olive, and slurring the days
    gone by,
When the poor are hovell'd and hustled together,
    each sex, like swine,
When only the ledger lives, and when only not all
    men lie ;
Peace in her vineyard—yes !—but a company forges
    the wine.

And the vitriol madness flushes up in the ruffian's
    head,
Till the filthy by-lane rings to the yell of the
    trampled wife,
And chalk and alum and plaster are sold to the
    poor for bread,
And the spirit of murder works in the very means
    of life.

And Sleep must lie down arm'd, for the villainous
    centre-bits
Grind on the wakeful ear in the hush of the moon-
    less nights,
While another is cheating the sick of a few last
    gasps, as he sits
To pestle a poison'd poison behind his crimson
    lights.

When a Mammonite mother kills her babe for a
    burial fee,
And Timour-Mammon grins on a pile of children's
    bones,
Is it peace or war ? better, war ! loud war by land
    and by sea,
War with a thousand battles, and shaking a hundred
    thrones.

For I trust if an enemy's fleet came yonder round
    by the hill,
And the rushing battle-bolt sang from the three-
    decker out of the foam,
That the smoothfaced snubnosed rogue would leap
    from his counter and till,
And strike, if he could, were it but with his cheating
    yardwand, home.——

What ! am I raging alone as my father raged in
    his mood ?
Must *I* too creep to the hollow and dash myself
    down and die
Rather than hold by the law that I made, never
    more to brood
On a horror of shatter'd limbs and a wretched
    swindler's lie ?

Would there be sorrow for *me* ? there was *love* in
    the passionate shriek,
Love for the silent thing that had made false haste
    to the grave—
Wrapt in a cloak, as I saw him, and thought he
    would rise and speak
And rave at the lie and the liar, ah God, as he used
    to rave.

I am sick of the Hall and the hill, I am sick of the
    moor and the main.
Why should I stay? can a sweeter chance ever come
    to me here?
O, having the nerves of motion as well as the nerves
    of pain,
Were it not wise if I fled from the place and the
    pit and the fear?

There are workmen up at the Hall : they are
    coming back from abroad ;
The dark old place will be gilt by the touch of a
    millionaire :
I have heard, I know not whence, of the singular
    beauty of Maud ;
I play'd with the girl when a child ; she promised
    then to be fair.

Maud with her venturous climbings and tumbles
    and childish escapes,
Maud the delight of the village, the ringing joy
    of the Hall,
Maud with her sweet purse-mouth when my father
    dangled the grapes,
Maud the beloved of my mother, the moon-faced
    darling of all,—

What is she now? My dreams are bad. She may
    bring me a curse.
No, there is fatter game on the moor ; she will let
    me alone.
Thanks, for the fiend best knows whether woman
    or man be the worse.
I will bury myself in my books, and the Devil may
    pipe his own.

II.

Long have I sigh'd for a calm : God grant I may
    find it at last !
It will never be broken by Maud, she has neither
    savour nor salt,
But a cold and clear-cut face, as I found when her
    carriage past,
Perfectly beautiful : let it be granted her : where
    is the fault ?
All that I saw (for her eyes were downcast, not to
    be seen)
Faultily faultless, icily regular, splendidly null,
Dead perfection, no more ; nothing more, if it had
    not been
For a chance of travel, a paleness, an hour's defect
    of the rose,
Or an underlip, you may call it a little too ripe,
    too full,
Or the least little delicate aquiline curve in a sensi-
    tive nose,
From which I escaped heart-free, with the least little
    touch of spleen.

III.

Cold and clear-cut face, why come you so cruelly
    meek,
Breaking a slumber in which all spleenful folly was
    drown'd,
Pale with the golden beam of an eyelash dead on
    the cheek,
Passionless, pale, cold face, star-sweet on a gloom
    profound ;

Womanlike, taking revenge too deep for a transient
    wrong

Done but in thought to your beauty, and ever as
    pale as before

Growing and fading and growing upon me without
    a sound,

Luminous, gemlike, ghostlike, deathlike, half the
    night long

Growing and fading and growing, till I could bear
    it no more,

But arose, and all by myself in my own dark garden
    ground,

Listening now to the tide in its broad-flung ship-
    wrecking roar,

Now to the scream of a madden'd beach dragg'd
    down by the wave,

Walk'd in a wintry wind by a ghastly glimmer,
    and found

The shining daffodil dead, and Orion low in his
    grave.

IV.

A million emeralds break from the ruby-budded
    lime

In the little grove where I sit—ah, wherefore cannot
    I be

Like things of the season gay, like the bountiful
    season bland,

When the far-off sail is blown by the breeze of a
    softer clime,

Half-lost in the liquid azure bloom of a crescent
    of sea,

The silent sapphire-spangled marriage ring of the
    land?

Below me, there, is the village, and looks how quiet
    and small !

And yet bubbles o'er like a city, with gossip, scandal,
    and spite ;

And Jack on his ale-house bench has as many lies as
    a Czar ;

And here on the landward side, by a red rock,
    glimmers the Hall ;

And up in the high Hall-garden I see her pass like
    a light ;

But sorrow seize me if ever that light be my leading
    star !

When have I bow'd to her father, the wrinkled head
    of the race ?

I met her to-day with her brother, but not to her
    brother I bow'd :

I bow'd to his lady-sister as she rode by on the
    moor ;

But the fire of a foolish pride flash'd over her
    beautiful face.

O child, you wrong your beauty, believe it, in being
    so proud ;

Your father has wealth well-gotten, and I am name-
    less and poor.

I keep but a man and a maid, ever ready to slander
    and steal ;

I know it, and smile a hard-set smile, like a stoic,
    or like

A wiser epicurean, and let the world have its
    way :

For nature is one with rapine, a harm no preacher
    can heal ;

The Mayfly is torn by the swallow, the sparrow
    spear'd by the shrike,
And the whole little wood where I sit is a world of
    plunder and prey.

We are puppets, Man in his pride, and Beauty fair
    in her flower ;
Do we move ourselves, or are moved by an unseen
    hand at a game
That pushes us off from the board, and others ever
    succeed ?
Ah yet, we cannot be kind to each other here for an
    hour ;
We whisper, and hint, and chuckle, and grin at a
    brother's shame ;
However we brave it out, we men are a little
    breed.

A monstrous eft was of old the Lord and Master of
    Earth,
For him did his high sun flame, and his river
    billowing ran,
And he felt himself in his force to be Nature's
    crowning race.
As nine months go to the shaping an infant ripe for
    his birth,
So many a million of ages have gone to the making
    of man :
He now is first, but is he the last ? is he not too
    base ?

The man of science himself is fonder of glory, and
    vain,

An eye well-practised in nature, a spirit bounded and
poor ;
The passionate heart of the poet is whirl'd into folly
and vice.
I would not marvel at either, but keep a temperate
brain ;
For not to desire or admire, if a man could learn it,
were more
Than to walk all day like the sultan of old in a
garden of spice.

For the drift of the Maker is dark, an Isis hid by
the veil.
Who knows the ways of the world, how God will
bring them about ?
Our planet is one, the suns are many, the world is
wide
Shall I weep if a Poland fall ? shall I shriek if a
Hungary fail ?
Or an infant civilisation be ruled with rod or with
knout ?
I have not made the world, and He that made it will
guide.

Be mine a philosopher's life in the quiet woodland
ways,
Where if I cannot be gay let a passionless peace be
my lot,
Far-off from the clamour of liars belied in the
hubbub of lies ;
From the long-neck'd geese of the world that are
ever hissing dispraise

Because their natures are little, and, whether he heed
  it or not,
Where each man walks with his head in a cloud of
  poisonous flies.

And most of all would I flee from the cruel madness
  of love,
The honey of poison-flowers and all the measureless ill.
Ah Maud, you milkwhite fawn, you are all unmeet
  for a wife.
Your mother is mute in her grave as her image in
  marble above ;
Your father is ever in London, you wander about
  at your will ;
You have but fed on the roses, and lain in the lilies
  of life.

v.

A voice by the cedar tree,
In the meadow under the Hall !
She is singing an air that is known to me,
A passionate ballad gallant and gay,
A martial song like a trumpet's call !
Singing alone in the morning of life,
In the happy morning of life and of May,
Singing of men that in battle array,
Ready in heart and ready in hand,
March with banner and bugle and fife
To the death, for their native land.

Maud with her exquisite face,
And wild voice pealing up to the sunny sky,

And feet like sunny gems on an English green,
Maud in the light of her youth and her grace,
Singing of Death, and of Honour that cannot die,
Till I well could weep for a time so sordid and mean,
And myself so languid and base.

Silence, beautiful voice!
Be still, for you only trouble the mind
With a joy in which I cannot rejoice,
A glory I shall not find.
Still! I will hear you no more,
For your sweetness hardly leaves me a choice
But to move to the meadow and fall before
Her feet on the meadow grass, and adore,
Not her, who is neither courtly nor kind,
Not her, not her, but a voice.

VI.

Morning arises stormy and pale,
No sun, but a wannish glare
In fold upon fold of hueless cloud,
And the budded peaks of the wood are bow'd
Caught and cuff'd by the gale:
I had fancied it would be fair.

Whom but Maud should I meet
Last night, when the sunset burn'd
On the blossom'd gable-ends
At the head of the village street,
Whom but Maud should I meet?
And she touch'd my hand with a smile so sweet,
She made me divine amends
For a courtesy not return'd.

And thus a delicate spark
Of glowing and growing light
Thro' the livelong hours of the dark
Kept itself warm in the heart of my dreams,
Ready to burst in a colour'd flame ;
Till at last when the morning came
In a cloud, it faded, and seems
But an ashen-gray delight.

What if with her sunny hair,
And smile as sunny as cold,
She meant to weave me a snare
Of some coquettish deceit,
Cleopatra-like as of old
To entangle me when we met,
To have her lion roll in a silken net
And fawn at a victor's feet.

Ah, what shall I be at fifty
Should Nature keep me alive,
If I find the world so bitter
When I am but twenty-five ?
Yet, if she were not a cheat,
If Maud were all that she seem'd,
And her smile were all that I dream'd,
Then the world were not so bitter
But a smile could make it sweet.

What if tho' her eye seem'd full
Of a kind intent to me,
What if that dandy-despot, he,
That jewell'd mass of millinery,
That oil'd and curl'd Assyrian Bull
Smelling of musk and of insolence,
Her brother, from whom I keep aloof,

Who wants the finer politic sense
To mask, tho' but in his own behoof,
With a glassy smile his brutal scorn—
What if he had told her yestermorn
How prettily for his own sweet sake
A face of tenderness might be feign'd,
And a moist mirage in desert eyes,
That so, when the rotten hustings shake
In another month to his brazen lies,
A wretched vote may be gain'd.

For a raven ever croaks, at my side,
Keep watch and ward, keep watch and ward,
Or thou wilt prove their tool.
Yea, too, myself from myself I guard,
For often a man's own angry pride
Is cap and bells for a fool.

Perhaps the smile and tender tone
Came out of her pitying womanhood,
For am I not, am I not, here alone
So many a summer since she died,
My mother, who was so gentle and good ?
Living alone in an empty house,
Here half-hid in the gleaming wood,
Where I hear the dead at midday moan,
And the shrieking rush of the wainscot mouse,
And my own sad name in corners cried,
When the shiver of dancing leaves is thrown
About its echoing chambers wide,
Till a morbid hate and horror have grown
Of a world in which I have hardly mixt,
And a morbid eating lichen fixt
On a heart half-turn'd to stone.

O heart of stone, are you flesh, and caught
By that you swore to withstand?
For what was it else within me wrought
But, I fear, the new strong wine of love,
That made my tongue so stammer and trip
When I saw the treasured splendour, her hand,
Come sliding out of her sacred glove,
And the sunlight broke from her lip?

I have play'd with her when a child;
She remembers it now we meet.
Ah well, well, well, I may be beguiled
By some coquettish deceit.
Yet, if she were not a cheat,
If Maud were all that she seem'd,
And her smile had all that I dream'd,
Then the world were not so bitter
But a smile could make it sweet.

VII.

Did I hear it half in a doze
    Long since, I know not where?
Did I dream it an hour ago,
  When asleep in this arm-chair?

Men were drinking together,
    Drinking and talking of me;
" Well, if it prove a girl, the boy
    Will have plenty: so let it be."

Is it an echo of something
    Read with a boy's delight,
Viziers nodding together
    In some Arabian night?

Strange, that I hear two men,
    Somewhere, talking of me ;
" Well, if it prove a girl, my boy
    Will have plenty : so let it be."

VIII.

She came to the village church,
And sat by a pillar alone ;
An angel watching an urn
Wept over her, carved in stone ;
And once, but once, she lifted her eyes,
And suddenly, sweetly, strangely blush'd
To find they were met by my own ;
And suddenly, sweetly, my heart beat stronger
And thicker, until I heard no longer
The snowy-banded, dilettante,
Delicate-handed priest intone ;
And thought, is it pride, and mused and sigh'd
" No surely, now it cannot be pride."

IX.

I was walking a mile,
More than a mile from the shore,
The sun look'd out with a smile
Betwixt the cloud and the moor.
And riding at set of day
Over the dark moor land,
Rapidly riding far away,
She waved to me with her hand.
There were two at her side,
Something flash'd in the sun,
Down by the hill I saw them ride,
In a moment they were gone :

Like a sudden spark
Struck vainly in the night,
Then returns the dark
With no more hope of light.

x.

Sick, am I sick of a jealous dread?
Was not one of the two at her side
This new-made lord, whose splendour plucks
The slavish hat from the villager's head?
Whose old grand-father has lately died,
Gone to a blacker pit, for whom
Grimy nakedness dragging his trucks
And laying his trams in a poison'd gloom
Wrought, till he crept from a gutted mine
Master of half a servile shire,
And left his coal all turn'd into gold
To a grandson, first of his noble line,
Rich in the grace all women desire,
Strong in the power that all men adore,
And simper and set their voices lower,
And soften as if to a girl, and hold
Awe-stricken breaths at a work divine,
Seeing his gewgaw castle shine,
New as his title, built last year,
There amid perky larches and pine,
And over the sullen-purple moor
(Look at it) pricking a cockney ear.

What, has he found my jewel out?
For one of the two that rode at her side
Bound for the Hall, I am sure was he:
Bound for the Hall, and I think for a bride.
Blithe would her brother's acceptance be,

Maud could be gracious too, no doubt,
To a lord, a captain, a padded shape,
A bought commission, a waxen face,
A rabbit mouth that is ever agape—
Bought ? what is it he cannot buy ?
And therefore splenetic, personal, base,
A wounded thing with a rancorous cry,
At war with myself and a wretched race,
Sick, sick to the heart of life, am I.

Last week came one to the county town,
To preach our poor little army down,
And play the game of the despot kings,
Tho' the state has done it and thrice as well :
This broad-brimm'd hawker of holy things,
Whose ear is stuff'd with his cotton, and rings
Even in dreams to the chink of his pence,
This huckster put down war ! can he tell
Whether war be a cause or a consequence ?
Put down the passions that make earth Hell !
Down with ambition, avarice, pride,
Jealousy, down ! cut off from the mind
The bitter springs of anger and fear ;
Down too, down at your own fireside,
With the evil tongue and the evil ear,
For each is at war with mankind.

I wish I could hear again
The chivalrous battle-song
That she warbled alone in her joy !
I might persuade myself then
She would not do herself this great wrong
To take a wanton dissolute boy
For a man and leader of men.

Ah God, for a man with heart, head, hand,
Like some of the simple great ones gone
For ever and ever by,
One still strong man in a blatant land,
Whatever they call him, what care I,
Aristocrat, democrat, autocrat—one
Who can rule and dare not lie.

And ah for a man to arise in me,
That the man I am may cease to be !

XI.

O let the solid ground
    Not fail beneath my feet
Before my life has found
    What some have found so sweet ;
Then let come what come may,
What matter if I go mad,
I shall have had my day.

Let the sweet heavens endure,
    Not close and darken above me
Before I am quite quite sure
    That there is one to love me ;
Then let come what come may
To a life that has been so sad,
I shall have had my day.

XII.

Birds in the high Hall-garden
    When twilight was falling,
Maud, Maud, Maud, Maud,
    They were crying and calling.

13

Where was Maud ? in our wood ;
   And I, who else, was with her,
Gathering woodland lilies,
   Myriads blow together.

Birds in our wood sang
   Ringing thro' the vallies,
Maud is here, here, here
   In among the lilies.

I kiss'd her slender hand,
   She took the kiss sedately ;
Maud is not seventeen,
   But she is tall and stately.

I to cry out on pride
   Who have won her favour !
O Maud were sure of Heaven
   If lowliness could save her.

I know the way she went
   Home with her maiden posy,
For her feet have touch'd the meadows
   And left the daisies rosy.

Birds in the high Hall-garden
   Were crying and calling to her,
Where is Maud, Maud, Maud ?
   One is come to woo her.

Look, a horse at the door,
   And little King Charles is snarling,
Go back, my lord, across the moor,
   You are not her darling.

XIII.

Scorn'd, to be scorn'd by one that I scorn,
Is that a matter to make me fret?
That a calamity hard to be borne?
Well, he may live to hate me yet.
Fool that I am to be vext with his pride!
I past him, I was crossing his lands;
He stood on the path a little aside;
His face, as I grant, in spite of spite,
Has a broad-blown comeliness, red and white,
And six feet two, as I think, he stands;
But his essences turn'd the live air sick,
And barbarous opulence jewel-thick
Sunn'd itself on his breast and his hands.

Who shall call me ungentle, unfair,
I long'd so heartily then and there
To give him the grasp of fellowship;
But while I past he was humming an air,
Stopt, and then with a riding whip
Leisurely tapping a glossy boot,
And curving a contumelious lip,
Gorgonised me from head to foot
With a stony British stare.

Why sits he here in his father's chair?
That old man never comes to his place:
Shall I believe him ashamed to be seen?
For only once, in the village street,
Last year, I caught a glimpse of his face,
A gray old wolf and a lean.
Scarcely, now, would I call him a cheat;

For then, perhaps, as a child of deceit,
She might by a true descent be untrue ;
And Maud is as true as Maud is sweet :
Tho' I fancy her sweetness only due
To the sweeter blood by the other side ;
Her mother has been a thing complete,
However she came to be so allied.
And fair without, faithful within,
Maud to him is nothing akin :
Some peculiar mystic grace
Made her only the child of her mother,
And heap'd the whole inherited sin
On that huge scapegoat of the race,
All, all upon the brother.

Peace, angry spirit, and let him be !
Has not his sister smiled on me ?

XIV.

Maud has a garden of roses
And lilies fair on a lawn ;
There she walks in her state
And tends upon bed and bower,
And thither I climb'd at dawn
And stood by her garden-gate ;
A lion ramps at the top,
He is claspt by a passion-flower.

Maud's own little oak-room
(Which Maud, like a precious stone
Set in the heart of the carven gloom,
Lights with herself, when alone
She sits by her music and books,

And her brother lingers late
With a roystering company) looks
Upon Maud's own garden gate :
And I thought as I stood, if a hand, as white
As ocean-foam in the moon, were laid
On the hasp of the window, and my Delight
Had a sudden desire, like a glorious ghost, to
    glide,
Like a beam of the seventh Heaven, down to
    my side,
There were but a step to be made.

The fancy flatter'd my mind,
And again seem'd overbold ;
Now I thought that she cared for me,
Now I thought she was kind
Only because she was cold.

I heard no sound where I stood
But the rivulet on from the lawn
Running down to my own dark wood ;
Or the voice of the long sea-wave as it swell'd
Now and then in the dim-gray dawn ;
But I look'd, and round, all round the house
    I beheld
The death-white curtain drawn ;
Felt a horror over me creep,
Prickle my skin and catch my breath,
Knew that the death-white curtain meant but
    sleep,
Yet I shudder'd and thought like a fool of
    the sleep of death.

xv.

So dark a mind within me dwells,
    And I make myself such evil cheer,
That if I be dear to some one else,
    Then some one else may have much to fear ;
But if I be dear to some one else,
    Then I should be to myself more dear.
Shall I not take care of all that I think,
Yea ev'n of wretched meat and drink,
If I be dear,
If I be dear to some one else.

xvi.

This lump of earth has left his estate
The lighter by the loss of his weight ;
And so that he find what he went to seek,
And fulsome Pleasure clog him, and drown
His heart in the gross mud-honey of town,
He may stay for a year who has gone for a week :
But this is the day when I must speak,
And I see my Oread coming down,
O this is the day !
O beautiful creature, what am I
That I dare to look her way ;
Think I may hold dominion sweet,
Lord of the pulse that is lord of her breast,
And dream of her beauty with tender dread,
From the delicate Arab arch of her feet
To the grace that, bright and light as the crest
Of a peacock, sits on her shining head,
And she knows it not : O, if she knew it,
To know her beauty might half undo it.

I know it the one bright thing to save
My yet young life in the wilds of Time,
Perhaps from madness, perhaps from crime,
Perhaps from a selfish grave.

What, if she be fasten'd to this fool lord,
Dare I bid her abide by her word?
Should I love her so well if she
Had given her word to a thing so low?
Shall I love her as well if she
Can break her word were it even for me?
I trust that it is not so.

Catch not my breath, O clamorous heart,
Let not my tongue be a thrall to my eye,
For I must tell her before we part,
I must tell her, or die.

XVII.

Go not, happy day,
    From the shining fields,
Go not, happy day,
    Till the maiden yields.
Rosy is the West,
    Rosy is the South,
Roses are her cheeks,
    And a rose her mouth.
When the happy Yes
    Falters from her lips,
Pass and blush the news
    Over the blowing ships.
Over blowing seas,
    Over seas at rest,

Pass the happy news,
  Blush it thro' the West ;
Till the red man dance
  By his red cedar tree,
And the red man's babe
  Leap, beyond the sea.
Blush from West to East,
  Blush from East to West,
Till the West is East,
  Blush it thro' the West.
Rosy is the West,
  Rosy is the South,
Roses are her cheeks,
  And a rose her mouth.

XVIII.

I have led her home, my love, my only friend.
There is none like her, none.
And never yet so warmly ran my blood
And sweetly, on and on
Calming itself to the long-wish'd-for end,
Full to the banks, close on the promised good.

None like her, none.
Just now the dry-tongued laurels' pattering talk
Seem'd her light foot along the garden walk,
And shook my heart to think she comes once
      more ;
But even then I heard her close the door,
The gates of Heaven are closed, and she is gone.

There is none like her, none.
Nor will be when our summers have deceased.
O, art thou sighing for Lebanon

In the long breeze that streams to thy delicious
    East,
Sighing for Lebanon,
Dark cedar, tho' thy limbs have here increased,
Upon a pastoral slope as fair,
And looking to the South, and fed
With honey'd rain and delicate air,
And haunted by the starry head
Of her whose gentle will has changed my fate,
And made my life a perfumed altar-flame ;
And over whom thy darkness must have spread
With such delight as theirs of old, thy great
Forefathers of the thornless garden, there
Shadowing the snow-limb'd Eve from whom she
    came.

Here will I lie, while these long branches sway,
And you fair stars that crown a happy day
Go in and out as if at merry play,
Who am no more so all forlorn,
As when it seem'd far better to be born
To labour and the mattock-harden'd hand,
Than nursed at ease and brought to understand
A sad astrology, the boundless plan
That makes you tyrants in your iron skies,
Innumerable, pitiless, passionless eyes,
Cold fires, yet with power to burn and brand
His nothingness into man.

But now shine on, and what care I,
Who in this stormy gulf have found a pearl
The countercharm of space and hollow sky,
And do accept my madness, and would die
To save from some slight shame one simple girl.

Would die ; for sullen-seeming Death may give
More life to Love than is or ever was
In our low world, where yet 'tis sweet to live.
Let no one ask me how it came to pass ;
It seems that I am happy, that to me
A livelier emerald twinkles in the grass
A purer sapphire melts into the sea.

Not die ; but live a life of truest breath,
And teach true life to fight with mortal wrongs.
O, why should Love, like men in drinking-songs,
Spice his fair banquet with the dust of death ?
Make answer, Maud my bliss,
Maud made my Maud by that long lover's kiss,
Life of my life, wilt thou not answer this ?
" The dusky strand of Death inwoven here
With dear Love's tie, makes Love himself more
    dear."

Is that enchanted moan only the swell
Of the long waves that roll in yonder bay ?
And hark the clock within, the silver knell
Of twelve sweet hours that past in bridal white,
And died to live, long as my pulses play ;
But now by this my love has closed her sight
And given false death her hand, and stol'n away
To dreamful wastes where footless fancies dwell
Among the fragments of the golden day.
May nothing there her maiden grace affright !
Dear heart, I feel with thee the drowsy spell.
My bride to be, my evermore delight,
My own heart's heart and ownest own farewell ;
It is but for a little space I go
And ye meanwhile far over moor and fell

Beat to the noiseless music of the night!
Has our whole earth gone nearer to the glow
Of your soft splendours that you look so bright?
I have climb'd nearer out of lonely Hell.
Beat, happy stars, timing with things below,
Beat with my heart more blest than heart can tell,
Blest, but for some dark undercurrent woe
That seems to draw—but it shall not be so :
Let all be well, be well.

XIX.

Her brother is coming back to-night,
Breaking up my dream of delight.

My dream? do I dream of bliss?
I have walk'd awake with Truth.
O when did a morning shine
So rich in atonement as this
For my dark dawning youth,
Darken'd watching a mother decline
And that dead man at her heart and mine :
For who was left to watch her but I?
Yet so did I let my freshness die.

I trust that I did not talk
To gentle Maud in our walk
(For often in lonely wanderings
I have cursed him even to lifeless things)
But I trust that I did not talk,
Not touch on her father's sin :
I am sure I did but speak
Of my mother's faded cheek,
When it slowly grew so thin,
That I felt she was slowly dying

Vext with lawyers and harass'd with debt :
For how often I caught her with eyes all wet,
Shaking her head at her son and sighing
A world of trouble within !

And Maud too, Maud was moved
To speak of the mother she loved
As one scarce less forlorn,
Dying abroad and it seems apart
From him who had ceased to share her heart,
And ever mourning over the feud,
The household Fury sprinkled with blood
By which our houses are torn :
How strange was what she said,
When only Maud and the brother
Hung over her dying bed—
That Maud's dark father and mine
Had bound us one to the other,
Betrothed us over their wine,
On the day when Maud was born ;
Seal'd her mine from her first sweet breath.
Mine, mine by a right, from birth till death,
Mine, mine—our fathers have sworn.

But the true blood spilt had in it a heat
To dissolve the precious seal on a bond,
That, if left uncancell'd, had been so sweet :
And none of us thought of a something beyond,
A desire that awoke in the heart of the child,
As it were a duty done to the tomb,
To be friends for her sake, to be reconciled ;
And I was cursing them and my doom,
And letting a dangerous thought run wild
While often abroad in the fragrant gloom

Of foreign churches—I see her there,
Bright English lily, breathing a prayer
To be friends, to be reconciled !

But then what a flint is he !
Abroad, at Florence, at Rome,
I find whenever she touch'd on me
This brother had laugh'd her down.
And at last, when each came home,
He had darken'd into a frown,
Chid her, and forbid her to speak
To me, her friend of the years before ;
And this was what had redden'd her cheek
When I bow'd to her on the moor.

Yet Maud, altho' not blind
To the faults of his heart and mind,
I see she cannot but love him,
And says he is rough but kind,
And wishes me to approve him,
And tells me, when she lay
Sick once, with a fear of worse,
That he left his wine and horses and play,
Sat with her, read to her, night and day,
And tended her like a nurse.

Kind ? but the death-bed desire
Spurn'd by this heir of the liar—
Rough but kind ?   Yet I know
He has plotted against me in this,
That he plots against me still.
Kind to Maud ? that were not amiss.
Well, rough but kind ; why, let it be so :
For shall not Maud have her will ?

For, Maud, so tender and true,
As long as my life endures
I feel I shall owe you a debt,
That I never can hope to pay ;
And if ever I should forget
That I owe this debt to you
And for your sweet sake to yours ;
O then, what then shall I say ?—
If ever I *should* forget,
May God make me more wretched
Than ever I have been yet !

So now I have sworn to bury
All this dead body of hate,
I feel so free and so clear
By the loss of that dead weight,
That I should grow light-headed, I fear,
Fantastically merry ;
But that her brother comes, like a blight
On my fresh hope, to the Hall to-night.

xx.

Strange, that I felt so gay,
Strange, that I tried to-day
To beguile her melancholy ;
The Sultan, as we name him,—
She did not wish to blame him—
But he vext her and perplext her
With his worldly talk and folly :
Was it gentle to reprove her
For stealing out of view
From a little lazy lover
Who but claims her as his due ?

Or for chilling his caresses
By the coldness of her manners,
Nay, the plainness of her dresses ?
Now I know her but in two,
Nor can pronounce upon it
If one should ask me whether
The habit, hat, and feather,
Or the frock and gipsy bonnet
Be the neater and completer ;
For nothing can be sweeter
Than maiden Maud in either.

But to-morrow, if we live,
Our ponderous squire will give
A grand political dinner
To half the squirelings near ;
And Maud will wear her jewels,
And the bird of prey will hover,
And the titmouse hope to win her
With his chirrup at her ear.

A grand political dinner
To the men of many acres,
A gathering of the Tory,
A dinner and then a dance
For the maids and marriage-makers,
And every eye but mine will glance
At Maud in all her glory.

For I am not invited,
But, with the Sultan's pardon,
I am all as well delighted,
For I know her own rose-garden,
And mean to linger in it
Till the dancing will be over ;

And then, oh then, come out to me
For a minute, but for a minute,
Come out to your own true lover,
That your true lover may see
Your glory also, and render
All homage to his own darling,
Queen Maud in all her splendour.

XXI.

Rivulet crossing my ground,
And bringing me down from the Hall
This garden-rose that I found,
Forgetful of Maud and me,
And lost in trouble and moving round
Here at the head of a tinkling fall,
And trying to pass to the sea ;
O Rivulet, born at the Hall,
My Maud has sent it by thee
(If I read her sweet will right)
On a blushing mission to me,
Saying in odour and colour, " Ah, be
Among the roses to-night."

XXII.

Come into the garden, Maud,
   For the black bat, night, has flown,
Come into the garden, Maud,
   I am here at the gate alone ;
And the woodbine spices are wafted abroad,
   And the musk of the roses blown.
For a breeze of morning moves,
   And the planet of Love is on high,

Beginning to faint in the light that she loves
　On a bed of daffodil sky,
To faint in the light of the sun she loves,
　To faint in his light, and to die.

All night have the roses heard
　The flute, violin, bassoon ;
All night has the casement jessamine stirr'd
　To the dancers dancing in tune ;
Till a silence fell with the waking bird,
　And a hush with the setting moon.

I said to the lily, " There is but one
　With whom she has heart to be gay.
When will the dancers leave her alone ?
　She is weary of dance and play."
Now half to the setting moon are gone,
　And half to the rising day ;
Low on the sand and loud on the stone
　The last wheel echoes away.

I said to the rose, " The brief night goes
　In babble and revel and wine.
O young lord-lover, what sighs are those,
　For one that will never be thine ?
But mine, but mine," so I sware to the rose,
　" For ever and ever, mine."

And the soul of the rose went into my blood,
　As the music clash'd in the hall ;
And long by the garden lake I stood,
　For I heard your rivulet fall
From the lake to the meadow and on to the wood,
　Our wood, that is dearer than all ;

From the meadow your walks have left so sweet
    That whenever a March-wind sighs
He sets the jewel-print of your feet
    In violets blue as your eyes,
To the woody hollows in which we meet
    And the valleys of Paradise.

The slender acacia would not shake
    One long milk-bloom on the tree ;
The white lake-blossom fell into the lake,
    As the pimpernel dozed on the lea ;
But the rose was awake all night for your sake,
    Knowing your promise to me ;
The lilies and roses were all awake,
    They sigh'd for the dawn and thee.

Queen rose of the rosebud garden of girls,
    Come hither, the dances are done,
In gloss of satin and glimmer of pearls,
    Queen lily and rose in one ;
Shine out, little head, sunning over with curls,
    To the flowers, and be their sun.

There has fallen a splendid tear
    From the passion-flower at the gate.
She is coming, my dove, my dear ;
    She is coming, my life, my fate ;
The red rose cries, " She is near, she is near ; "
    And the white rose weeps, " She is late ; "
The larkspur listens, " I hear, I hear ; "
    And the lily whispers, " I wait."

She is coming, my own, my sweet ;
    Were it ever so airy a tread,
My heart would hear her and beat,
    Were it earth in an earthy bed ;

My dust would hear her and beat,
　　Had I lain for a century dead ;
　Would start and tremble under her feet,
　　And blossom in purple and red.

XXIII.

" The fault was mine, the fault was mine "—
Why am I sitting here so stunn'd and still,
Plucking the harmless wild-flower on the hill ?—
It is this guilty hand !—
And there rises ever a passionate cry
From underneath in the darkening land—
What is it, that has been done ?
O dawn of Eden bright over earth and sky,
The fires of Hell brake out of thy rising sun,
The fires of Hell and of Hate ;
For she, sweet soul, had hardly spoken a word,
When her brother ran in his rage to the gate,
He came with the babe-faced lord ;
Heap'd on her terms of disgrace,
And while she wept, and I strove to be cool,
He fiercely gave me the lie,
Till I with as fierce an anger spoke,
And he struck me, madman, over the face,
Struck me before the languid fool,
Who was gaping and grinning by :
Struck for himself an evil stroke ;
Wrought for his house an irredeemable woe ;
For front to front in an hour we stood,
And a million horrible bellowing echoes broke
From the red-ribb'd hollow behind the wood,
And thunder'd up into Heaven the Christless code,
That must have life for a blow.

Ever and ever afresh they seem'd to grow.
Was it he lay there with a fading eye?
" The fault was mine," he whisper'd, " fly!"
Then glided out of the joyous wood
The ghastly Wraith of one that I know;
And there rang on a sudden a passionate cry,
A cry for a brother's blood:
It will ring in my heart and my ears, till I die,
    till I die.

Is it gone? my pulses beat—
What was it? a lying trick of the brain?
Yet I thought I saw her stand,
A shadow there at my feet,
High over the shadowy land.
It is gone; and the heavens fall in a gentle rain,
When they should burst and drown with deluging
    storms
The feeble vassals of wine and anger and lust,
The little hearts that know not how to forgive:
Arise, my God, and strike, for we hold Thee just,
Strike dead the whole weak race of venomous worms,
That sting each other here in the dust;
We are not worthy to live.

XXIV.

See what a lovely shell,
Small and pure as a pearl,
Lying close to my foot,
Frail, but a work divine,
Made so fairily well
With delicate spire and whorl,
How exquisitely minute,
A miracle of design!

What is it ? a learned man
Could give it a clumsy name.
Let him name it who can,
The beauty would be the same.

The tiny cell is forlorn,
Void of the little living will
That made it stir on the shore.
Did he stand at the diamond door
Of his house in a rainbow frill ?
Did he push, when he was uncurl'd,
A golden foot or a fairy horn
Thro' his dim water-world ?

Slight, to be crush'd with a tap
Of my finger-nail on the sand,
Small, but a work divine,
Frail, but of force to withstand,
Year upon year, the shock
Of cataract seas that snap
The three decker's oaken spine
Athwart the ledges of rock,
Here on the Breton strand !

Breton, not Briton ; here
Like a shipwreck'd man on a coast
Of ancient fable and fear—
Plagued with a flitting to and fro,
A disease, a hard mechanic ghost
That never came from on high
Nor ever arose from below,
But only moves with the moving eye,
Flying along the land and the main—
Why should it look like Maud ?

Am I to be overawed
By what I cannot but know
Is a juggle born of the brain ?

Back from the Breton coast,
Sick of a nameless fear,
Back to the dark sea-line
Looking, thinking of all I have lost ;
An old song vexes my ear ;
But that of Lamech is mine.

For years, a measureless ill,
For years, for ever, to part—
But she, she would love me still ;
And as long, O God, as she
Have a grain of love for me,
So long, no doubt, no doubt,
Shall I nurse in my dark heart,
However weary, a spark of will
Not to be trampled out.

Strange, that the mind, when fraught
With a passion so intense
One would think that it well
Might drown all life in the eye,—
That it should, by being so overwrought,
Suddenly strike on a sharper sense
For a shell, or a flower, little things
Which else would have been past by !
And now I remember, I,
When he lay dying there,
I noticed one of his many rings
(For he had many, poor worm) and thought
It is his mother's hair.

Who knows if he be dead?
Whether I need have fled?
Am I guilty of blood?
However this may be,
Comfort her, comfort her, all things good,
While I am over the sea!
Let me and my passionate love go by,
But speak to her all things holy and high,
Whatever happen to me!
Me and my harmful love go by;
But come to her waking, find her asleep,
Powers of the height, Powers of the deep,
And comfort her tho' I die.

XXV.

Courage, poor heart of stone!
I will not ask thee why
Thou canst not understand
That thou art left for ever alone:
Courage, poor stupid heart of stone.—
Or if I ask thee why,
Care not thou to reply:
She is but dead, and the time is at hand
When thou shalt more than die.

XXVI.

O that 'twere possible
After long grief and pain
To find the arms of my true love
Round me once again!

When I was wont to meet her
In the silent woody places

By the home that gave me birth,
We stood tranced in long embraces
Mixt with kisses sweeter sweeter
Than anything on earth.

A shadow flits before me,
Not thou, but like to thee ;
Ah Christ, that it were possible
For one short hour to see
The souls we loved, that they might tell us
What and where they be.

It leads me forth at evening,
It lightly winds and steals
In a cold white robe before me,
When all my spirit reels
At the shouts, the leagues of lights,
And the roaring of the wheels.

Half the night I waste in sighs,
Half in dreams I sorrow after
The delight of early skies ;
In a wakeful dose I sorrow
For the hand, the lips, the eyes,
For the meeting of the morrow,
The delight of happy laughter,
The delight of low replies.

'Tis a morning pure and sweet,
And a dewy splendour falls
On the little flower that clings
To the turrets and the walls ;
'Tis a morning pure and sweet
And the light and shadow fleet ;

She is walking in the meadow,
And the woodland echo rings ;
In a moment we shall meet ;
She is singing in the meadow,
And the rivulet at her feet
Ripples on in light and shadow
To the ballad that she sings.

Do I hear her sing as of old,
My bird with the shining head,
My own dove with the tender eye ?
But there rings on a sudden a passionate cry,
There is some one dying or dead,
And a sullen thunder is roll'd ;
For a tumult shakes the city,
And I wake, my dream is fled ;
In the shuddering dawn, behold,
Without knowledge, without pity,
By the curtains of my bed
That abiding phantom cold.

Get thee hence, nor come again,
Mix not memory with doubt,
Pass, thou deathlike type of pain,
Pass and cease to move about,
'Tis the blot upon the brain
That *will* show itself without.

Then I rise, the eavedrops fall,
And the yellow vapours choke
The great city sounding wide ;
The day comes, a dull red ball
Wrapt in drifts of lurid smoke
On the misty river-tide.

Thro' the hubbub of the market
I steal, a wasted frame,
It crosses here, it crosses there,
Thro' all that crowd confused and loud,
The shadow still the same ;
And on my heavy eyelids
My anguish hangs like shame.

Alas for her that met me,
That heard me softly call,
Came glimmering thro' the laurels
At the quiet evenfall,
In the garden by the turrets
Of the old manorial hall.

Would the happy spirit descend,
From the realms of light and song,
In the chamber or the street,
As she looks among the blest,
Should I fear to greet my friend
Or to say " forgive the wrong "
Or to ask her, " take me, sweet,
To the regions of thy rest " ?

But the broad light glares and beats
And the shadow flits and fleets
And will not let me be ;
And I loathe the squares and streets,
And the faces that one meets,
Hearts with no love for me :
Always I long to creep
Into some still cavern deep,
There to weep, and weep, and weep
My whole soul out to thee.

XXVII.

Dead, long dead,
Long dead !
And my heart is a handful of dust,
And the wheels go over my head,
And my bones are shaken with pain,
For into a shallow grave they are thrust,
Only a yard beneath the street,
And the hoofs of the horses beat, beat,
The hoofs of the horses beat,
Beat into my scalp and my brain,
With never an end to the stream of passing feet,
Driving, hurrying, marrying, burying,
Clamour and rumble, and ringing and clatter,
And here beneath it is all as bad,
For I thought the dead had peace, but it is not so ;
To have no peace in the grave, is that not sad ?
But up and down and to and fro,
Ever about me the dead men go ;
And then to hear a dead man chatter
Is enough to drive one mad.

Wretchedest age, since Time began,
They cannot even bury a man ;
And tho' we paid our tithes in the days that are gone,
Not a bell was rung, not a prayer was read ;
It is that which makes us loud in the world of
          the dead ;
There is none that does his work, not one ;
A touch of their office might have sufficed,
But the churchmen fain would kill their church,
As the churches have kill d their Christ.

See, there is one of us sobbing,
No limit to his distress ;
And another, a lord of all things, praying,
To his own great self, as I guess ;
And another, a statesman there, betraying
His party-secret, fool, to the press ;
And yonder a vile physician, blabbing
The case of his patient—all for what?
To tickle the maggot born in an empty head,
And wheedle a world that loves him not,
For it is but a world of the dead.

Nothing but idiot gabble !
For the prophecy given of old
And then not understood,
Has come to pass as foretold ;
Not let any man think for the public good,
But babble, merely for babble.
For I never whisper'd a private affair
Within the hearing of cat or mouse,
No, not to myself in the closet alone,
But I heard it shouted at once from the top of the
        house ;
Everything came to be known :
Who told *him* we were there ?

Not that gray old wolf, for he came not back
From the wilderness, full of wolves, where he
        used to lie ;
He has gather'd the bones for his o'er-grown
        whelp to crack ;
Crack them now for yourself, and howl, and die.

Prophet, curse me the blabbing lip,
And curse me the British vermin, the rat;
I know not whether he came in the Hanover ship,
But I know that he lies and listens mute
In an ancient mansion's crannies and holes:
Arsenic, arsenic, sure, would do it,
Except that now we poison our babes, poor souls!
It is all used up for that.

Tell him now; she is standing here at my head;
Not beautiful now, not even kind;
He may take her now; for she never speaks her
    mind,
But is ever the one thing silent here.
She is not of us, as I divine;
She comes from another stiller world of the dead,
Stiller, not fairer than mine.

But I know where a garden grows,
Fairer than aught in the world beside,
All made up of the lily and rose
That blow by night, when the season is good,
To the sound of dancing music and flutes:
It is only flowers, they had no fruits,
And I almost fear they are not roses, but blood;
For the keeper was one, so full of pride,
He linkt a dead man there to a spectral bride;
For he, if he had not been a Sultan of brutes,
Would he have that hole in his side?

But what will the old man say?
He laid a cruel snare in a pit
To catch a friend of mine one stormy day;

Yet now I could even weep to think of it ;
For what will the old man say
When he comes to the second corpse in the pit ?

Friend, to be struck by the public foe,
Then to strike him and lay him low,
That were a public merit, far,
Whatever the Quaker holds, from sin ;
But the red life spilt for a private blow—
I swear to you, lawful and lawless war
Are scarcely even akin.

O me, why have they not buried me deep enough ?
Is it kind to have made me a grave so rough,
Me, that was never a quiet sleeper ?
Maybe still I am but half-dead ;
Then I cannot be wholly dumb ;
I will cry to the steps above my head
And somebody, surely, some kind heart will come
To bury me, bury me
Deeper, ever so little deeper.

XXVIII.

My life has crept so long on a broken wing
Thro' cells of madness, haunts of horror and fear,
That I come to be grateful at last for a little thing :
My mood is changed, for it fell at a time of year
When the face of night is fair on the dewy downs,
And the shining daffodil dies, and the Charioteer
And starry Gemini hang like glorious crowns
Over Orion's grave low down in the west,
That like a silent lightning under the stars

She seem'd to divide in a dream from a band of the
    blest,
And spoke of a hope for the world in the coming
    wars—
"And in that hope, dear soul, let trouble have rest,
Knowing I tarry for thee," and pointed to Mars
As he glow'd like a ruddy shield on the Lion's breast.

And it was but a dream, yet it yielded a dear delight
To have look'd, tho' but in a dream, upon eyes so fair,
That had been in a weary world my one thing bright ;
And it was but a dream, yet it lighten'd my despair
When I thought that a war would arise in defence of
    the right,
That an iron tyranny now should bend or cease,
The glory of manhood stand on his ancient height,
Nor Britain's one sole God be the millionaire :
No more shall commerce be all in all, and Peace
Pipe on her pastoral hillock a languid note,
And watch her harvest ripen, her herd increase,
Nor the cannon-bullet rust on a slothful shore,
And the cobweb woven across the cannon's throat
Shall shake its threaded tears in the wind no more.

And as months ran on and rumour of battle grew,
" It is time, it is time, O passionate heart," said I
(For I cleaved to a cause that I felt to be pure and
    true),
" It is time, O passionate heart and morbid eye,
That old hysterical mock-disease should die."
And I stood on a giant deck and mix'd my breath
With a loyal people shouting a battle cry,
Till I saw the dreary phantom arise and fly
Far into the North, and battle, and seas of death.

Let it go or stay, so I wake to the higher aims
Of a land that has lost for a little her lust of gold,
And love of a peace that was full of wrongs and
    shames,
Horrible, hateful, monstrous, not to be told ;
And hail once more to the banner of battle unroll'd !
Tho' many a light shall darken, and many shall weep
For those that are crush'd in the clash of jarring
    claims,
Yet God's just wrath shall be wreak'd on a giant liar;
And many a darkness into the light shall leap,
And shine in the sudden making of splendid names,
And noble thought be freer under the sun,
And the heart of a people beat with one desire ;
For the peace, that I deem'd no peace, is over and
    done,
And now by the side of the Black and the Baltic
    deep,
And deathful-grinning mouths of the fortress, flames
The blood-red blossom of war with a heart of fire.

Let it flame or fade, and the war roll down like a
    wind,
We have proved we have hearts in a cause, we are
    noble still,
And myself have awaked, as it seems, to the better
    mind ;
It is better to fight for the good, than to rail at the ill;
I have felt with my native land, I am one with my
    kind,
I embrace the purpose of God, and the doom assign'd.